SHELLEY

AN INEFFECTUAL ANGEL?

Cat. 200 Posthumous head of Shelley, carved by Marianne Hunt

I should conceive no one so difficult to pourtray, the expression of his countenance being ever flitting and varied, - now depressed and melancholy, now lit up like that of a spirit, - making him look one moment forty and the next eighteen.

- Thomas Medwin, *Life of Shelley*

SHELLEY

AN INEFFECTUAL ANGEL?

Robert Woof

THE WORDSWORTH TRUST
1992

Cover illustration   Portrait of Shelley by Amelia Curran (*National Portrait Gallery*)

Copyright 1992 The Wordsworth Trust
All rights reserved
Typeset by The Wordsworth Trust
Printed by Titus Wilson & Son, Kendal

IBSN 1 870787 00 5

Contents

Lenders to the Exhibition

Lord Abinger
David Alexander
Iain Bain
Geoffrey Bindman
The British Library
Cooper Art Gallery, Barnsley
Roy Davids
Eton College
Eton School
David Gardner-Medwin
Kenneth Garlick
The Laing Art Gallery, Newcastle upon Tyne
John Murray
National Portrait Gallery, London
Newstead Abbey, Nottinghamshire
Dallas Pratt
Reading Museum
Tennyson Research Centre, Lincolnshire County Council
Chris Titterington
Derek Wise
Jonathan Wordsworth
Edward Yardley

Among the generous owners who have lent to the Exhibition several wish to remain anonymous.

Acknowledgments

The Wordsworth Trust would like to thank all those who have made possible this Exhibition celebrating the bicentenary of the birth of Percy Bysshe Shelley. Organised by the Wordsworth Trust at the Centre for British Romanticism, Dove Cottage, Grasmere, it ran at the Wordsworth Museum from 28 July to 1 November 1992, and, in a slightly reduced form, at the British Library from 4 December to 28 February 1993.

The lenders are formally listed elsewhere, but their contribution was clearly a major one. The most important source has been the British Library, whose collection of Shelley and his circle (much of it now in the Ashley Collection, the gift of T.J. Wise, bibliographer and forger), is full of treasures. The British Library staff have facilitated the Exhibition throughout, but I must mention especially Jane Carr, Head of Exhibitions, her colleague Alan Sterenberg, and not least Shelley Jones, the skilled presenter and the intrepid traveller. Janet Backhouse, Sally Brown, and Elizabeth James all made what were quite difficult arrangements seem easy, and selected the final core of the exhibition for the British Library.

Any presentation of Shelley must take Byron into account. We have had the great good fortune to have the advice and enthusiasm of John G. Murray of the publishing house that bears his name and that of his famous ancestor, and which still flourishes in Albemarle Street, even as it did in the days of Byron and Shelley.

Eton College has two fine collections. The College Collection under Paul Quarrie gave us admirable insight into the history and curriculum of the school in Shelley's time. It was Paul Quarrie's acumen that led to the finding of the hitherto unrecorded fact that Shelley took part in the Ad Montem ceremony. Michael Meredith, of the School Library, provided two great icons: the 'sulking' head of the poet carved by Marianne Hunt, and the more sombre Death Mask of Keats taken in Rome.

Throughout the portraits have been illuminating. We are grateful to the National Portrait Gallery, and especially to Kai Kin Yung and Tim Morton, for helping with the selection of portraits of the Shelley Circle. To their collection we are indebted, as we also are to Newstead Abbey and Nottingham County Council for the loan of the portrait of Claire Clairmont, and to one anonmyous lender for the marvellous Harlow portrait of Byron, so rarely exhibited. Lord Abinger has lent two key images, one being the miniature of Mary Wollstonecraft after Oppé, and the other being the small quarto portfolio portrait of Shelley after Amelia Curran. David Alexander, always generous, supplied crucial prints of Godwin, Mary Wollstonecraft and of Shelley himself. The Tennyson Research Centre, Lincolnshire County Council, provided the photograph by Julia Margaret Cameron of May Princep enacting Beatrice Cenci, a brilliant allusion to the design of the 'Guido Reni' portrait.

The landscapes include three ravishing watercolours from the Laing Art Gallery at Newcastle upon Tyne by William Pars, Peter De Wint and Samuel Prout. Ed Yardley gave us access to his Turner prints; and Giles Omar-Parsons, Keeper of Fine and Applied Art at Reading Museum and Art Gallery, arranged for us to borrow two series of prints of the River Thames, the one by Joseph Farington, the other by William Havell. The Alpine Club of Great Britain supplied the William Pars engraving of Mont Blanc. Jonathan Wordsworth's 'Ancient Beech-Tree, Windsor Great Park' by Paul Sandby and Iain Bain's landscapes by Edward Finden and by William Daniel helped illustrate the wandering life that Shelley and his family lived.

There are others who have helped over many years. The first of these is Charles Warren, one of our Trustees, who has greatly enriched our Shelley Collection, so that it now embraces Thomas Peacock, J.W. Polidori, and Mary Shelley, as well as Shelley himself. Peter Butter, formerly Regius Professor at Glasgow, and Jo Manton, in honour of her late husband Robert Gittings, have both enriched our collections with the editions of scholarly works.

Others have helped through their scholarly perception. These include Gerald Burdon, Roy Davids, Michael Kitson, Dallas Pratt, Chris Titterington, Derek Wise.

From the staff at Grasmere there has been dedicated support, which includes the kindness of those who allowed their colleagues to concentrate on the Shelley project. But among those who must be named are: Michael McGregor, over two years, built up the data of what we could borrow; Jeff Cowton, the meticulous Registrar, was helped throughout by Joanne Gunnion and David Green. Several helped with the typing, but especially Sally Woodhead, my personal assistant, and Henry Wordsworth. It is to Stephen Hebron that I am most indebted. Working with Oliver Turnbull at Titus Wilson, he has designed and created the catalogue as a desktop publishing project. Moreover he has drafted notes, edited others, and given the whole project a guardianship. The errors are my own, but the success that the exhibition has had owes much to Stephen's exemplary work. Finally, whatever understanding I have of Shelley comes from conversations with Pamela, my wife, and her insights will be found throughout.

This catalogue is published with the help of Mr Peter Placito, the Paul Mellon Centre for Studies in British Art and the Binks Trust. The Wordsworth Trustees are grateful for these donations. We are also grateful for the offer of sponsorship to support the exhibition from Titus Wilson & Son, Kendal, Cumbria.

Introduction

> Wordsworth and Byron stand, it seems to me, first and pre-eminent in actual performance, a glorious pair among the English poets of this century. Keats had probably, indeed, a more consummate poetic gift than either of them; but he died having produced too little and being as yet too immature to rival them. I for my part can never even think of equalling with them any other of their contemporaries; - either Coleridge, poet and philosopher wrecked in a mist of opium; or Shelley, beautiful and ineffectual angel, beating in the void his luminous wings in vain. Wordsworth and Byron stand out by themselves. When the year nineteen hundred is turned, and our nation comes to recount our poetic glories in the century which has then just ended, the first names with her will be these.

This famous and perhaps reckless judgement by Matthew Arnold in attempting to rank the English Romantic poets is so assertive that it immediately pleads to be questioned. And hence, the title of this publication and of the exhibition it accompanies, is in the interrogative mode. Arnold's remarks were indeed soon to be debated, and in 1886, five years after Arnold's publication of his essay (as a preface to his selection of Byron's poems), the Reverend Stopford Brooke gave his "Inaugural Address" to the new Shelley Society. His conclusion too was assertive, and it opposed Arnold's; in his view, Shelley was supreme as a spokesman for modern oppressed and hitherto inarticulate men:

> Were society to alter, as it must soon alter or disintegrate, away from this condition [of despair], and live more in the hopes, and with the aims, and in the simple life, of Shelley, and along with these possess also his sanity of view, it would then understand how foolish it is to call him "a beautiful, but ineffectual angel, beating in the void his luminous wings in vain." Towards that change, his work in poetry concerning man is one element of power; but I fear that those who move too far apart from the more ideal hopes of man, in the midst of a formulated culture, will not see or understand that this is true. They think that *Welt Geist* moves most vividly, most effectually, in the educated part of society. I do not think that their opinion is true; nor indeed has history testified to that, but to the very contrary. This life of the World Spirit, now in England, is most vivid in the ideas, hopes and passionate feelings which, unformed, are yet taking form, in the poor, the overworked, the oppressed ... If you wish to be in the forefront of the future, if you wish to live in the ideas which will, thirty years hence, rule the world, live among the men who are indignant and who hope with Shelley, who have his faith, who hear the trumpet of a prophecy, and whose cry day and night is this.

> O, wind,
If winter comes, can spring be far behind?

It is in the nature of Shelley's achievement that it should provoke debate. A hundred years on from Arnold and Brooke it still provokes debate. Why has this poet not 'settled down'? This celebration of Shelley's life and work has questions behind it, and these will occur to the viewer of the exhibition, the reader of this guide, and the reader of Shelley's poetry. Shelley himself was a continuing debater. Many of his poems end with unanswered questions. Does anything at all lie behind that sublime summit of Mont Blanc that he visited with Mary in 1816?

> And what were thou, and earth, and stars, and sea,
> If to the human mind's imaginings
> Silence and solitude were vacancy?

Again, the autumnal west wind provokes him to ask if there will be a new world order, how long will it be before the change happens? 'If Winter comes, can Spring be far behind?'

Putting an hypothesis, placing an 'if', is a way of seeing how deeply tangled are the boughs of Heaven and Ocean, and life itself. There is no simplification of this. The West Wind is at once Destroyer and Preserver; the poet is both the supplicant of the wind, 'O hear', 'Make me thy lyre', and the only force that can give powerful meaning to the natural energy that is everywhere, the wind:

> Scatter, as from an unextinguished hearth
> Ashes and sparks, my words among mankind!

Shelley's words have scattered, and reading them we are in the middle of the tumult of mighty harmonies. There is no resting. There is no joy for us human beings without the immediacy of pain.

> We look before and after,
> And pine for what is not -
> Our sincerest laughter
> With some pain is fraught -
> Our sweetest songs are those that tell of saddest thought.

What ignorance of pain must a skylark have that it can sing with such a flood of rapture? There are no fixed states and certainties for humans.

If Shelley's Prometheus learns through pain to renounce vindictiveness, Beatrice Cenci must spring from Shelley's pen even before *Prometheus* is completed to explore the terrible consequences on the soul of what might so reasonably be deemed a justifiable vengeance. Again, if there is a surging sense that the injustices of social life will be removed, as Shelley suggests in *The Masque of Anarchy* - 'Ye are many - they are few', there is also the dark knowledge that the 'marble brow of youth was cleft -

> With care, and in the eyes where once hope shone
> Desire like a lioness bereft
> Of its last cub, glared ere it died.

If there is the idealistic Maddalo, there is the more sceptical Julian, and a poem that cannot conclude, that leaves the effects of love, even to madness upon the soul, unrevealed to the reader:

> I urged and questioned still, she told me how
> All happened - but the cold world shall not know.

Perhaps one of the greatnesses of Shelley is that he has no hankering to solve the mysteries. He brings us close to the whole perplexity - in religion, in love, in politics, in life:

> 'Then, what is Life?' I said . . .

This is from Shelley's last piece of writing, a fragment, and the poem closes as the cripple begins, but fails to answer.

Always Shelley brings us close to the consuming questions of who and why we are. We do not go to him for answers - except in that the questions themselves are in a way answers, for they make us face the inexplicable marvellousness of being alive.

> I see a mighty Darkness
> Filling the seat of power; and rays of gloom
> Dart round, as light from the meridian Sun,
> Ungazed upon and shapeless - neither limb
> Nor form - nor outline, yet we feel it is
> A living Spirit.

We do feel the living Spirit. This is darkness that can be seen; it can give off rays, like light that is itself ungazed on; it has no definition, yet it lives. Shelley thus excites the mind with oppositions, paradox, with difficulties. And his language reflects the mysteries he will not simplify. He has to be articulate about thoughts that cannot, of their nature, be single and clear. They spring from the world we can all see, the world of yellow bees i' the ivy-bloom, but not directly; they are refracted through a mind that is haunted by wildernesses of thought. The poet,

> Nor seeks nor finds he mortal blisses,
> But feeds on the aërial kisses
> Of shapes that haunt thought's wildernesses.
> He will watch from dawn to gloom
> The lake-reflected sun illume
> The yellow bees i' the ivy-bloom
> Nor heed nor see, what things they be;
> But from these create he can
> Forms more real than living man,
> Nurslings of immortality!

In creating those forms Shelley takes his reader into the wildernesses of thought. To read *Mont Blanc* is to muse with Shelley upon 'my own, my human mind', to be with his mind in action, and use, as his mind does, as ours do, without explanation, the things we see as the matter and exercise of thought. The ravine, the river and the mountain move in and out of the mind as Shelley looks on the real landscape about Mont Blanc, and using only the language of landscape, with no extended abstractions or conceptual expressions, he takes us through what must be hailed as a philosophical exciting exercise on the nature of mind, of power, of the sublime, of imagination, of the possible divine. He scarcely uses such words; he thinks in images. He is a true poet.

The images can be contained in a single line or little more:

> It is the unpastured Sea hung'ring for Calm.
> Peace, Monster - I come now!

And all the longing and the need for peace of a world that has been too long under the domination of a tyrant is evoked, and given relief. Again, images can tumble one after another into a verse; that unseen power, the mind's creative imagination, Intellectual Beauty, comes to us inexplicably and of its own wayward accord:

> Like hues and harmonies of evening, -
>   Like clouds in starlight widely spread, -
>   Like memory of music fled, -
>   Like aught that for its grace may be
> Dear, and yet dearer for its mystery.

Each simile, seeking to evoke something elusive, speaks of phenomena, themselves each more and more elusive, first, outside the mind - the evening harmonies and night clouds, then, inside - the memory of past music, and finally, something so elusive and ever mysterious that it cannot be named. In another example, *To a Skylark*, a rain of melodies simply showers from an unseen bird in the form of verse after verse of images that evoke spontaneous profusion, like the Poet

>   hidden
> In the light of thought
> Singing hymns unbidden.

Or the maiden singing to herself for love, or the rose that cannot help giving its scent to the wind. And so it goes on; images express Shelley's thought.

In large structures Shelley similarly thinks in images. *Prometheus Unbound* is built upon the restoration of a family. When Prometheus has endured long upon his frozen rock and the birds of Jupiter have torn him into continual pain, he reaches a point when he no longer wishes his original curse upon the unjust Jupiter to be effective. He recalls the curse, is free of it, and is therefore ready to be freed himself. But he cannot be released without love, and this active love comes from his wife, Asia, far away. Like a spirit of spring, she goes down with her sister into the deepest cave of the Mother Earth, sees the mysterious Demogorgon who knows that the time has come and that there is in things a need and a necessity for change. Thus Asia, the wife, frees the husband, and the Spirit of the Earth who is, as it were, their child, is joyful. The lyric drama sees that harmony for the whole universe is possible; one can simply think of it as a family restored. Beethoven had used this idea literally some ten years earlier; Leonora dressed as the youth Fidelio rescues her husband, a political prisoner. The Prisoners emerge into the light, and joy, again as at the end of the Ninth Symphony, is the triumphant closure of restoration through love.

But the family riven apart must be the inverse of *Prometheus Unbound* and Shelley is compelled, and at the same time, - to explore this. For there is no stasis. The father here is not cosmic, not Jupiter. His power is over his family and its ultimate expression in subduing his wife, sons and daughter is in raping that daughter. Beatrice Cenci goes nearly mad, but she has spirit and she plans the murder of her father. This is finally carried out, but alas, need not have been, for shortly, we discover, the Count Cenci would have been apprehended officially. Beatrice, in attacking violent evil with the weapons of violence, in murdering, has become herself tainted like her father. She is 'wrapped in a strange cloud of crime and shame' and has achieved nothing. The alternative way of Prometheus

> To forgive wrongs darker than Death or Night,
> To defy Power which seems Omnipotent;
> To love, and bear;

seems the better way - for the family, and for society, the larger family.

There is a family presence and a moving one even in *Adonais*, the formal elegy for Keats. The young Keats, the poet, is half Adonis and his death thus sacrificial; but he is also Shelley's own creation, not Adonis but Adonais, mourned not by a lover, Venus, but by, foremost among others, a mother, Urania, the Muse of Heavenly Poetry. Keats, in death, is seen as belonging,

> He is made one with Nature: there is heard
> His voice in all her music . . .

His grave on earth is in Rome, that city which is at once Paradise and wilderness. 'Go thou to Rome' writes Shelley, and to

> a slope of green access
> Where, like an infant's smile, over the dead,
> A light of laughing flowers along the grass is spread.

Near that light of flowers Keats is buried, and the flowers, we realise, cover the graves of Shelley's and Mary's eldest son William who had died in Rome not two years before, in June 1819. Thus *Adonais* is implicitly a poem for Mary too; it expresses a mother's grief and offers consolation, before ending on that fearful note of solitude for Shelley himself,

> I am borne darkly, fearfully, afar.

Human relationships move beyond the family; and friendship and love are equally important themes for Shelley. The riding and talking with Byron outside Venice is celebrated in *Julian and Maddalo*. A spaciousness and ease of relationship is mirrored in the free conversational couplets. Shelley is fully himself

> I love all waste
> And solitary places; where we taste
> The pleasure of believing what we see
> Is boundless, as we wish our souls to be:

He is also entirely sociable,

> - as we rode, we talked; and the swift thought,
> Winging itself with laughter, lingered not,
> But flew from brain to brain.

The Letter to Maria Gisborne is an even more informal expression of friendship. For the Gisbornes in London Shelley evokes their study in their house near Livorno:

> A pretty bowl of wood - not full of wine,
> But quicksilver . . .
> A heap of rosin, a queer broken glass
> With ink in it; - a china cup that was
> What it will never be again, I think, . . .
> Near that a dusty paint-box, some odd hooks,
> A half-burnt match, an ivory block, three books, . . .

And as he thinks of the Gisbornes in England, he paints one of his hellish images of London for himself:

> - a shabby stand
> Of Hackney coaches, a brick house or wall
> Fencing some lonely court, white with the scrawl
> Of our unhappy politics; - or worse -
> A wretched woman reeling by, whose curse
> Mixed with the watchman's, partner of her trade,
> You must accept in place of serenade -

Shelley's perception of the actual world is precise and telling. This is the London of that earlier radical poet, Blake, with whom of course Shelley has much in common: the loathing of tyranny, the hatred of father figures as they wield power.

Friendship brings a conversational tone to Shelley's verse; sexual and romantic love demands a higher, or a more lyric, style. The tensions and the wonders of love are explored most fully in *Epipsychidion*, and here too, feelings are brought out, not hidden or glossed over. For a moment or two, even in the final description of triumphant love, there might be a calmness:

> We two will rise, and sit, and walk together,
> Under the roof of blue Ionian weather
> . . . .
> Possessing and possessed by all that is
> Within that calm circumference of bliss,
> . . . .
> And we will talk, until thought's melody
> Become too sweet for utterance, and it die
> In words . . .

And thus the words move into looks and action, and Shelley, surely as well as any writer of the erotic, suggests sexual consummation, culminating in

> One Heaven, one Hell, one immortality,
> And one annihilation.

The process is an image of the constant need for renewal. After such flight of fire -

> I pant, I sink, I tremble, I expire!

And it all must, like the wind, the seasons, the cloud, political movements, start again. The Cloud laughs at its own cenotaph:

> And out of the caverns of rain,
> Like a child from the womb, like a ghost from the tomb,
> I arise and unbuild it again.

Shelley constantly rises again, builds and unbuilds, and the energy that drives him is, in a most essential way, sexual.

It is certainly natural. The medium of political ideas and philosophic thinking is in images that are natural forces, whether sexual, familial, the storms and winds of air, the mountains of the earth, the high stars or the rivers. When a later poet, Yeats, thought about Shelley he thought about rivers, and how, for Shelley, the mind itself moved like a river. Shelley's own understanding of this will be explored in the opening chapter. Here, one might note that from the early *Alastor* onwards, the journey along and up a river, is a way, without using such words, of talking about origins. For the poet in *Alastor* the journey ends in extinction, the quest never completed. The water on which the poet in *Adonais*, perhaps again Shelley himself, is finally embarked is the sea, and his 'spirit's bark is driven / Far from the shore'.

This brings us in a kind of way full circle. But as we have thought with Shelley and felt the power of his imagery and gone so far with him in the uncharted psychological exploration, and found along the way such music and so many permanent images that are ours too, we can only praise the courage and honesty of the man, and love the artist. It was Wordsworth whom Shelley never met who said of the young poet that he had been 'one of the best *artists* of us all'. And it has been fitting that an exhibition celebrating Shelley should have its own origins by the rivers and hills of the English Lake District.

A Shelley Chronology

1792

Percy Bysshe Shelley born on 4 August at Field Place, near Horsham in Sussex. His father, Sir Timothy Shelley, is a Whig member of Parliament, and his grandfather Sir Bysshe Shelley, a wealthy landowner. He grows up in the company of four admiring sisters, and is taught by the local clergyman, the Reverend Evan Edwards.

1802

Shelley sent to Syon House Academy at Isleworth, near London. His cousin and future biographer, Thomas Medwin, is also at the school. 'This place was a perfect hell to Shelley,' Medwin recalled. 'I think I see him now - along the southern wall, indulging in various vague and undefined ideas, the chaotic elements, if I may say so, of what afterwards produced so beautiful a world.' Shelley first hears Adam Walker lecture at Syon House on contemporary science.

1804

Shelley is sent to Eton, where, as at Syon House Academy, his life is complicated by the bullying activities of fellow pupils. A sympathetic schoolmaster, Dr James Lind, helps him attain an unusually good knowledge of Latin and Greek, and introduces him to radical politics. In 1805 Shelley takes part in the Ad Montem Ceremony and in 1809 Dr Joseph Goodall is succeeded as headmaster by Dr John 'Flogger' Keate, who imposes new standards of discipline on the school.

1810

In the spring Shelley publishes *Zastrozzi*, 'by P.B.S.', an exuberant if artless Gothic novel, and is paid £40 for the work. He spends the money on a banquet for eight of his friends at Eton. A second book, *Original Poetry* 'by Victor and Cazire', is published in the autumn, but unluckily it includes a poem by M.G. Lewis, and is quickly withdrawn. Shelley leaves Eton and in October enters University College, Oxford. He meets Thomas Jefferson Hogg, and in November they jointly publish *Posthumous Fragments of Margaret Nicholson*. A second Gothic novel, *St. Irvyne*, is published in December. Both Shelley and Hogg are known for their independent opinions and eccentric behaviour.

1811

In January Shelley meets his future wife, the fifteen year-old Harriet Westbrook. In February he and Hogg write a small pamphlet entitled *The Necessity of Atheism*. Its publication promptly ends their Oxford careers after only two terms. This, and his subsequent elopement to Edinburgh with Harriet Westbrook in August, leads to Shelley's lasting estrangement from his father. The Shelleys move to York, and then to Keswick in the Lake District. Shelley visits Greystoke near Penrith, the home of the Whig peer the Duke of Norfolk, and there meets William Calvert, who introduces him to the future Poet Laureate, Robert Southey. He is unable to see either Wordsworth or Coleridge (or Thomas De Quincey, a relative newcomer to the Lakes and a later admirer of Shelley).

1812

In February Shelley goes to Dublin to distribute his pamphlet *An Address to the Irish People*, furthering the cause of Catholic Emancipation. After delivering a public address at the Fishamble Street Theatre, his political activities begin to be monitored by Home Office spies. A second pamphlet, *Proposals for an Association of Philanthropists*, and a broadside, *A Declaration of Rights* are also published in February. He returns from Dublin in April, moves to Lynmouth, a coastal village in North Devon, and begins his long poem *Queen Mab*. He then moves to Tremadoc in North Wales and joins a scheme to build an embankment across an estuary. In October he meets in London the radical philosopher William Godwin, so celebrated a figure for the earlier generation of Romantic poets.

1813

Following a violent attack on his house, Shelley leaves Tremadoc in February, makes a second trip to Ireland. He returns to London in April. Two hundred and fifty copies of *Queen Mab* are issued in May, and on 23 June his first child, Ianthe Shelley, is born. In July the Shelleys move to Bracknell, near Windsor.

1814

Shelley separates from Harriet and in July elopes with Mary Wollstonecraft Godwin, daughter of William Godwin and Mary Wollstonecraft. Mary's step-sister Jane, later known as Claire Clairmont, accompanies them on their continental journey, acting as interpreter. After travelling through France, Switzerland and Germany they return on 13 September. The trip is later recounted by Mary Shelley in *History of a Six Weeks' Tour* (1817). Shelley's son Charles is born to Harriet on 30 November.

1815

Shelley's grandfather, Sir Bysshe Shelley, dies on 5 January. Three years earlier Shelley had written: 'He is a bad man. I never had any respect for him, I always regarded him as a curse on society.I shall not grieve at his death.' In August the Shelleys move to Bishopsgate, near Windsor Great Park, and Shelley begins work on his first major poem, *Alastor*. He, Mary Shelley, Charles Clairmont and the poet and satirical novelist Thomas Love Peacock take a boat up the Thames, finding it impassable after Lechlade.

1816

Shelley's son by Mary, William, is born on 24 January. In February *Alastor* is published, the volume also containing his sonnet *To Wordsworth*. In March and April, Claire Clairmont has a brief affair with Lord Byron. On 3 May Shelley, Mary Shelley and Claire (who is now carrying Byron's child) set out for Switzerland. On the shore of Lake Geneva Shelley is introduced to Lord Byron, who is staying nearby at the Villa Diodati with his volatile travelling physician, John William Polidori. On 17 June, at Byron's suggestion, the party agree to write a ghost story each, and soon afterwards Mary Shelley begins *Frankenstein*. The Shelleys visit Chamonix, see Mont Blanc and climb to the Mer de Glace. Shelley writes his great poem *Mont Blanc*. On 8 September they return to England and live in London. In October Mary's half-sister, Fanny Imlay, commits suicide in Swansea, and a month later Harriet Shelley (then heavily pregnant) drowns herself in the Serpentine. Shelley marries Mary on 30 December, but later fails to get custody of his children by Harriet.

1817

Allegra, Claire Clairmont's daughter by Byron, is born on 12 January. The Shelleys move to Marlow in Buckinghamshire in March and settle there. Shelley expands his friendships with writers, including those with Leigh Hunt, poet and editor of the *Examiner*, Horace Smith and, significantly, John Keats. *A Proposal for Putting Reform to the Vote* is published in March. In September Shelley begins *Rosalind and Helen* and finishes *Laon and Cythna* (published in December but withdrawn and reissued in January the following year as *The Revolt of Islam*). Clara Shelley is born on 2 September. In a sonnet competition with Horace Smith, Shelley writes 'Ozymandias'.

1818

The Shelleys leave for the Continent on 11 March, and Shelley never returns to England. In April they reach Milan, move to Livorno, where they meet John and Maria Gisborne, and then to the Bagni de Lucca. In April Shelley helps arrange that Allegra join Byron in Venice. He translates Plato's *Sym-*

posium, and at Mary's request, completes *Rosalind and Helen* (published in spring 1819). In September the Shelleys go to Venice, and there Shelley renews his friendship with Lord Byron. Clara Shelley dies at Venice on 24 September. At Este, Shelley begins *Julian and Maddalo*, 'Lines written in the Euganean Hills', and the first act of *Prometheus Unbound*. In December the Shelleys move to Naples.

1819

The Shelleys leave Naples in February, and move to Rome. There Shelley writes the second and third acts of *Prometheus Unbound* and begins *The Cenci*. William Shelley dies on 7 June. In September, after hearing news from England of the Peterloo Massacre, writes the 'The Masque of Anarchy' at Livorno. In October they move to Florence and a second son, Percy Florence is born on 12 November, the only child destined to outlive his father. Shelley writes his parody of Wordsworth, *Peter Bell the Third*, 'Ode to the West Wind' and the prose work, *A Philosophical View of Reform*. He completes the fourth act of *Prometheus Unbound*, and the poem is published in August the following year; `It is the most perfect of my productions', he writes to his publisher Charles Ollier.

1820

The Shelleys move to Pisa and, after a brief period at Livorno, settle there. Over the next two years an English circle is established, including Lord Byron, Thomas Medwin, Edward and Jane Williams and Edward John Trelawny. In August, at the nearby Baths of San Giuliano, Shelley writes 'The Witch of Atlas,' and *Swellfoot the Tyrant* (published and suppressed in December).

1821

Shelley writes his semi-autobiographical poem on love, *Epipsychidion*, in January–February, and the poem is published anonymously in May. Prompted by Peacock's satirical *The Four Ages of Poetry*, Shelley writes *A Defence of Poetry*. News of Keats's death in Rome on 23 February reaches Shelley nearly two months later. From June to July he is engaged in writing *Adonais*, published immediately in Pisa. In October he writes his last published work, *Hellas*.

1822

Shelley writes his poems to Jane Williams, and begins his last, unfinished poem, 'The Triumph of Life'. Allegra Byron dies on 28 April. In April the Shelleys and the Williamses move to San Terenzo near Lerichi, and Shelley receives his boat, the *Ariel* (known also as the *Don Juan*) on 12 May. On 1 June he and Williams (and the boat-boy, Charles Vivien) sail to Livorno to meet Leigh Hunt, and on 8 July they drown in a storm on the return voyage.

'Poesy's unfailing River'

Much of Shelley's time in England, from his schooldays at Isleworth and Eton and his two terms at Oxford, to his years at Windsor and Marlow between 1815 and 1818, was spent near the banks of the Thames. Images of the Thames, either those by Joseph Farington celebrating fine houses in their great estates, or those by William Havell portraying working life on the river itself, give some idea of how the river was regarded in Shelley's lifetime. Arguably, the less open and more secretive images from J.M.W. Turner, or from his namesake, William Turner of Oxford, give a more essential image of the kind of river Shelley evokes in, say, his poem *Alastor* (1816). Shelley there represents the quest of the poet as a journey up a river. His poem (perhaps based on his half-praise, half-disappointment in Wordsworth) concludes with a fine elegiac note, recognising that the poet - who must by definition pursue the ideal - only finds rest from that haunting imperative in death. Though the Arab maiden offers him practical help and human love, that is not enough to satisfy the poet's needs; the mysterious Alastor, the 'spirit of solitude', is the equivalent of Wordsworth's 'the sounding cataract haunted . . . like a passion'. For Shelley the searching was the philosophical activity; the journey itself, often upstream in a search for origins, was the proper pursuit of the poet.

In the river Shelley found a suitable symbol for the restless movement of his intellectual and poetic ambition. 'Rivers are not like roads', he wrote to his friend Thomas Love Peacock in July 1816, 'the work of the hands of man; they imitate mind, which wanders at will over pathless deserts, and flows through nature's loveliest recesses, which are inaccessible to anything besides.' A year earlier Peacock, along with Mary Shelley and Charles Clairmont, had accompanied Shelley on a memorable tour up the Thames as far as Lechlade, where the river became too shallow to provide them with a secure channel. 'Our voyage terminated at a spot where the cattle stood entirely across the stream,' he wrote, 'with the water scarcely covering their hooves.' Shelley's adventurous hope had been that they could travel by various waterways as far as the Falls of Clyde, a distance by water of some two thousand miles. In later life Shelley spent a great deal of time on the Serchio, near Pisa, and in his poem *The Boat on the Serchio* he describes the feelings of excitement and possibility that the river inspired:

> But the clear stream in full enthusiasm
> Pours itself on the plain, then wandering
>   Down one clear path of effluence crystalline
> Sends its superfluous waves, that they may fling
>   At Arno's feet tribute of corn and wine;
> Then, through the pestilential deserts wild
>   Of tangled marsh and woods of stunted pine,
> It rushes to the ocean.

Many of the most astute critics found Shelley's 'full enthusiasm' difficult to appreciate. 'You, I am sure, will forgive me for sincerely remarking that you might curb your magnanimity and be more of an artist, and load every rift of your subject with ore' Keats wrote to Shelley in August 1820. Certainly Shelley could cascade ideas and images, so that, as W.B. Yeats said of *Mont Blanc*, 'the poetry is so overladen with descriptions in parentheses that one loses sight of its logic', but one has to respond to that plenitude. Yeats concludes:

> I think too that as he knelt before an altar where a thin flame burnt in a lamp made of green agate, a single vision would have come to him again and again, a vision of a boat drifting down a broad river between high hills where there were caves and towers, and following the light of one Star; and that voices would have told him told him how there is for every man some one scene, some one adventure, some one picture that is the image of his secret life, for wisdom first speaks in images. . .

Cat. 2 (viii.)

1
J.C. Stadler after Joseph Farington
Views of the River Thames
Published 1 June 1793
Hand-coloured engravings
19 x 30 cms
READING MUSEUM

i.   *Culham Court*
ii.   *Wallingford*
iii. *Streatley and Goring*
iv.   *Whitchurch*
v.   *Scene at Park Place including The Druid's Temple*
vi.   *View of Reading from Caversham*
vii. *Buscot-Park*

2
R. & D. Havell after William Havell
Views of the River Thames
Published 1 May 1811
Hand-coloured engravings
35 x 50 cms
READING MUSEUM

i.   *An Island on the Thames near Park Place Oxfordshire*
ii.   *The Weir, from Marlow Bridge*
iii. *Caversham Bridge, near Reading*
iv.   *View of Taplow, from Maidenhead Bridge*

v.   *Clifden Spring and Woods, near Maidenhead*
vi.   *Datchet Ferry, near Windsor*
vii. *Staines Church, with the City Stone on the Banks of the Thames*
viii. *Oxford, from the Banks of the Isis*

Cat. 3

3
R. Wallis after J.M.W. Turner
On the Thames
Engraving
16 x 27.5 cms
EDWARD YARDLEY COLLECTION

Turner stayed regularly at Sion Ferry House, Isleworth between 1804-5, perhaps while Shelley was still at Syon House Academy, and from there made many sketching trips along the Thames.

Prelude: The French Revolution

Shelley was born at Field Place, Sussex on 4 August 1792, son of Whig MP Sir Timothy Shelley, and grandson of Sir Bysshe Shelley, a wealthy landowner. He grew up in the reactionary period of English politics dominated by the war against Napoleon, but his mind looked to the earlier, more optimistic days of the French Revolution. In his pamphlet *A Proposal for An Association of Philanthropists* (1812) he wrote:

> In the revolution of France, were engaged men, whose names are inerasible from the records of Liberty. Their genius penetrated with a glance the gloom and glare which Church-craft and State-craft had spread before the imposture and villainy of their establishments. They saw the world, were they men? Yes! They felt for it! They risked their lives and happiness for its benefit!

This leap back to revolutionary ideals was noticed with surprise by one former radical, Robert Southey, in 1812. 'Here is a man at Keswick, who acts upon me as my own ghost would do', he wrote to Grosvenor C. Bedford on 4 January, 'He is just what I was in 1794. His name is Shelley, son to the member for Shoreham; with 6000*l*. a year entailed upon him, and as much more in his father's power to cut off . . . I tell him that all the difference between us is that he is nineteen, and I am thirty-seven; and I daresay it will not be very long before I shall succeed in convincing him that he may be a true philosopher, and do a great deal of good, with 6000*l*. a year; the thought of which troubles him a great deal more at present than ever the want of sixpence (for I have known such a want) did me.'

During the revolutionary period, a number of anti-government societies were formed in England, and many English writers and intellectuals, including Tom Paine, John Thelwall, William Godwin and Mary Wollstonecraft, held sympathies that were strongly pro-French. These earlier idealistic pamphleteers were largely pilloried or condemned by the English establishment, but Shelley drew enthusiastically from their legacy when formulating his own radical ideas.

4
Pedigree of Percy Bysshe Shelley
17 June 1880
DEREK WISE COLLECTION

Attested by Sir Timothy Shelley and John Shelley Sidney in 1816, the pedigree traces the Shelley line back to a Henry Shelley, of Worminghurst, Sussex, who died in 1612. It was not until 1806, however, when Shelley's grandfather, Bysshe Shelley, was made a baronet, that the family achieved any public distinction (and Sir Bysshe, a self-made man with atheistic principles and a childhood spent in America, was hardly a part of the English aristocracy).

Cat. 5

5
William Godwin (1756-1836)
Engraving by George Dawe after James Northcote
Published 4 October 1802
Mezzotint 37 x 30 cms
DAVID ALEXANDER COLLECTION

William Godwin was an enthusiastic supporter of the principles of the French Revolution. He achieved fame in 1793 when he published *An Enquiry Concerning Political Justice*, a work which made him the intellectual spokesman for English radicalism. Shelley confidently introduced himself to Godwin in a letter of 3 January 1812, the day after Southey had written about him to Bedford (see above):

> The name of Godwin has been used to excite in me feelings of reverence and admiration, I have been accustomed to consider him a luminary too dazzling for the darkness which surrounds him, and from the earliest period of my knowledge of his principles I have ardently desired to share on the footing of intimacy that intellect which I have delighted to contemplate in its emanations.

After Shelley's flight in 1814 to the continent with Godwin's daughter Mary, the two men's relations were less than ideal, concerned mostly with money matters.

6
William Godwin
Portrait by H.W. Pickersgill
1830
Oil on canvas 69.9 x 63.2 cms
NATIONAL PORTRAIT GALLERY, LONDON

A major portrait painter, Pickersgill tended to choose his subjects when they were famous, and therefore in their more elderly state. The matter-of-fact view he took of his sitters is seen in this portrait of a scantily-haired and white-eyebrowed Godwin, and even more in the image of Byron's former mistress Teresa Guiccioli (entry no. 155), painted in 1833 during her visit to England (her cheeks a little too red, her ringlets a little too girlish).

7*
William Godwin
An Enquiry Concerning Political Justice
Dublin: Luke White, 1793
THE WORDSWORTH TRUST [THE BRITISH LIBRARY BOARD]

Going beyond Paine's 'common-sense' call for political freedom, *Political Justice* condemns economic inequality and urges for a reform based on the need to use reason as a source of decision and, logically enough, on non-violence. It is possible that Shelley read the book at Eton, and by 1812 he is urging his friend Elizabeth Hitchener to read it (significantly in its first, more outspoken edition). That same year he wrote to Godwin:

> It is now a period of more than two years since first I saw your inestimable book on 'Political Justice'. It opened to my mind fresh & more extensive views; it materially influenced my character, and I rose from its perusal a wiser and a better man. I was no longer the votary of Romance; till then I had existed in an ideal world; now I found that in this universe of ours was enough to excite the interest of the heart, enough to employ the discussions of Reason; I beheld in short that I had duties to perform. - Conceive the effect which the Political Justice would have upon a mind before jealous of its independence and participating somewhat singularly in a peculiar susceptibility.

8
Thomas Holcroft (left) and William Godwin at the Treason Trials, 1794
Portrait by Sir Thomas Lawrence
1794
Pencil 15.3 x 12.2 cms
KENNETH GARLICK COLLECTION

1794 saw the end of the Great Terror in France, when thousands had been put to death in the name of the people. The authorities in England were quick to react, charging certain prominent radicals and French sympathizers with treason (a capital offence). Those prosecuted included Horne Tooke, John Thelwall and Godwin's friend Thomas Holcroft, and the eventual acquittal of the last was much helped by Godwin's urgent pamphlet, *Cursory Strictures on the Charge delivered by Lord Chief Justice Eyre to the Grand Jury.* As soon as the charges against him were dropped, Holcroft rose from the dock and sat beside the author for the remainder of the trial.

Cat. 8

9
William Godwin
Letter to William Wordsworth
London, 5 March 1811
THE WORDSWORTH TRUST

When Shelley met Godwin in 1812 the famous philosopher was 56 years old and a spent intellectual force. After his marriage to Mary Jane Clairmont in 1801, he had been faced with the unfamiliar burden of having to support a wife and five children, and so was forced into the publishing business. A stream of successful children's books followed, and here Godwin asks Wordsworth to versify 'The Beauty and the Beast'.

A story which Mʳˢ. Godwin has fixed upon is that of La Belle & le Bete, one of the most interesting & delicate tales my childhood ever knew. Could we interest you so far in our welfare, as to prevail on you to try to put it into verse? I need not tell you that the success would entirely depend upon its suiting a certain class of readers, that is, upon its exhibiting as much delicate simplicity as you please, but nothing abstruse, nothing that would repel the young, or wrinkle with the frown of investigation the forehead of the fair. It should be comprised in somewhat less than thrice hurried verses,

& must inevitably be in a sort of smooth & flowing rhythm.

10
William Wordsworth (1770-1850)
Letter to William Godwin
Grasmere, 9 March 1811
THE WORDSWORTH TRUST

Godwin's letter drew from the poet both an icy distaste for the theme of the tale and a charming, comic brightness in which he chides Godwin for his thoughtlessness over the high cost of small packets in the post.

I cannot work upon the suggestion of others however eagerly I might have addressed myself to the proposed subject if it had come to me of its own accord. You will therefore attribute my declining the task of versifying the Tale to this infirmity, rather than to an indisposition to serve you. Having stated this, it is unnecessary to add, that in my opinion things of this sort cannot be even decently done without great labour, especially in our language.... I confess there is to me something disgusting in the notion of a human Being consenting to *Mate* with a Beast, however amiable his qualities of heart. There is a line and a half in the Paradise Lost upon this subject which always shocked me,
     'for which cause
   Among the Beasts no Mate for thee was found.'
These are objects to which the attention of the mind ought not to be turned even as things in possibility. I have never seen the Tale in french, but as every body knows, the word Bete in french conversation perpetually occurs as applied to a stupid, senseless, half idiotic Person bêtise in like manner stands for stupidity. With us Beast and bestial excite loathsome and disgusting ideas; I mean when applied in a metaphorical manner; and consequently something of the same hangs about the literal sense of the words. *Brute* is the word employed when we contrast the intellectual qualities of the inferior animals with our own, the brute creation, etc. 'Ye of *brute human*, we of *human Gods*.' Brute metaphorically used, with us designates ill-manners of a coarse kind, or insolent and ferocious cruelty I make these remarks with a view to the difficulty attending the treatment of this story in our tongue, I mean in verse, where the utmost delicacy, that is, true philosophic permanent delicacy is required.
   ...Permit me to add one particular. You live and have lived long in London and therefore may not know at what rate Parcels are conveyed by Coach. Judging from the diminutive size of yours, you probably thought the expence of it would be trifling. You remember the story of the poor Girl who being reproached with having brought forth an illegitimate Child said it was true, but added that it was a very little one; insinuating thereby that her offence was small in proportion. But the plea does not hold good. As it is in these cases of morality so is it with the Rules of the Coach Offices. To be brief, I had to pay for your tiny parcel 4/9 and should have no more to pay if it had been 20 times as large. The weight till it amount to several pounds is no object with these People; a small Parcel requires as much trouble to receive, to lodge, and to deliver as a large one, and probably more *care* on account of its very smallness. I deem you therefore from inattention or want of knowledge my debtor, and will put you in a way of being quits with me.

Cat. 12

11*
Mary Wollstonecraft (1759-1797)
Portrait after John Opie
Miniature H 7 cms
LORD ABINGER COLLECTION

Opie's portrait shows Mary Wollstonecraft in 1797, the year she married William Godwin. She was then pregnant with her second child, Mary Wollstonecraft Godwin, and was to die, shortly after giving birth, of puerperal fever.

12
Mary Wollstonecraft
Engraving by W.T. Annis after John Opie
Published 1 June 1802
Mezzotint 25.4 x 20.3 cms
DAVID ALEXANDER COLLECTION

13*
Mary Wollstonecraft
A Vindication of the Rights of Woman
London: J. Johnson, 1792
THE WORDSWORTH TRUST [THE BRITISH LIBRARY BOARD]

Published in 1792, the year of Shelley's birth, *A Vindication of the Rights of Woman* made its author, according to Godwin, for a while the most famous woman in Europe. Her early 'feminist' position sees a woman's increased rights as an integral part of an ideal future state and therefore links the position of women closely with current social conditions and assumptions. Free from the constraints of royalty, militarism, church hierarchy and the 'legal

prostitution' of marriage, women would be, like men, perfectible, but at present 'trifling employments have rendered woman a trifler'. Opponents of the work like Horace Walpole were alarmed not so much by its 'feminism' as by the force of its social criticism and the visionary scope of its politics.

14
William Hazlitt (1778-1830)
Portrait by William Bewick
1825
Chalk 48 x 33.5 cms
THE WORDSWORTH TRUST

Hazlitt shared many of Shelley's political opinions, but he distrusted the young poet's rather flamboyant brand of radicalism. In his 1821-2 essay 'On Paradox and Commonplace', he wrote:

> . . . The author of the *Prometheus Unbound* (to take an individual instance of the last character) has a fire in his eye, a fever in his blood, a maggot in his brain, a hectic flutter in his speech, which mark out the philosophic fanatic. He is sanguine-complexioned, and shrill-voiced. As is often observable in the case of religious enthusiasts, there is a slenderness of constitutional *stamina*, which renders the flesh no match for the spirit. His bending, flexible form appears to take no strong hold of things, does not grapple with the world about him, but slides from it like a river . . . '

This insult, Shelley, so fascinated by rivers, might well have taken as a compliment.

Cat. 14

Education: 1792-1811

Shelley entered Syon House Academy in 1802 as, in his own words to Godwin, 'the votary of Romance': 'I was haunted with a passion for the wildest and most extravagant romances. Ancient books of Chemistry and Magic were perused with an enthusiasm of wonder, almost amounting to belief. My sentiments were unrestrained by anything within me'. Nine years later he left Oxford a dedicated radical, determined to take an active part in the political affairs of the country, and the Gothic tales of M.G. Lewis and Mrs Radcliffe were put aside for Godwin's *Political Justice*. 'I had existed in an ideal world', he wrote to Godwin, 'now I found that in this universe of ours was enough to excite the interest of the heart, enough to employ the discussions of Reason. I beheld in short that I had duties to perform.

Early biographers, concerned with the young Shelley's heroic resistance to the brutalities of the nineteenth century public school system, have given his solitude at Syon House and Eton an almost mythological importance. 'Shelley came among his fellow-creatures, congregated for the purposes of education, like a spirit from another sphere', wrote Mary Shelley in 1839, and his cousin Thomas Medwin remembered him at Syon House 'pacing, with rapid strides, a favourite and remote spot of the playground, generally alone. Yet Shelley left Eton well-prepared - intellectually confident, inquisitive about science, and well-educated in the classics, he had found a sympathetic tutor in the figure of Dr. James Lind, the seventy-year Royal Physician to the King, and it is possible that Lind may have introduced him to Godwin's *Political Justice*.

Shelley took part in several more conformist activities, most notably the Ad Montem Ceremony, a ritual not wholly unlike a modern rag day, when money was begged from passers-by, including the King and Queen; on his final day at Eton he recited Cicero's condemnation of Cataline in Speeches (final speech day). Already a published author, he had recently spent the £40 he received for *Zastrozzi* on a leaving dinner for his friends.

On Shelley's arrival at Oxford in October 1810 his father introduced him to the local booksellers, Slatter and Munday: 'My son here, has a literary turn; he is already an author, and do pray indulge him in his printing freaks'. It was one such 'printing freak', a small pamphlet entitled *The Necessity of Atheism*, that dramatically cut short his career at the University after only two terms. One of the first publications openly to challenge atheism in England, it ultimately led to an unbridgeable estrangement from his college, his father and his family, but its avowed atheism is an early instance of Shelley's poetic and religious concern with the problem of how to express the inexpressible. 'I call him a man of religious mind, because every audacious negative cast up by him against the Divine, was incorporated with a mood of reverence and adoration.' writes Robert Browing in his *Essay on Shelley*, and nine years later Shelley wrote in *A Defence of Poetry* (1820) that 'Poetry redeems from decay the visitations of the divinity in man . . . it purges from our inward sight the film of familiarity which obscures us from the wonder of our being.'

Samuel Heironymous Grimm, *Field Place*

Cat. 2 (vii) R & D Havell after William Havell, *Staines Church from the Thames*

Cat. 18 Stadler after Pugin, *Eton Schoolroom*

Cat. 32 Joseph Farington, *View of High-Street Oxford*

Cat. 16

15

J.C. Stadler after Joseph Farington
Eaton
Published J. & J. Boydell: London, 1 June 1793
Aquatint 18.5 x 29 cms
ETON COLLEGE COLLECTION

A view of Eton from the East, with the chapel on the left and the college buildings to the right. Also shown is the college wharf, no longer standing, to which all heavy goods, including books, were delivered.

16*

J.C. Stadler after William Westall
Eton College from the River
Published by R. Ackermann:
London, 1 March 1816
Aquatint 18.5 x 27.5 cms
ETON COLLEGE COLLECTION

One of forty-eight plates illustrating *The History of the Colleges of Winchester, Eton and Westminster* by W. Combe. Ten of the plates, including entry no. 18 (below), are of Eton.

17

Joseph Farington (1747-1821)
The Playground at Eton College in Buckinghamshire
Pencil, watercolour and wash 17.5 x 24.3 cms
ETON COLLEGE COLLECTION

A group of boys are shown playing cricket from the playing field, a place much celebrated by Thomas Gray, Farington's favourite poet, in his 'Ode on a distant Prospect of Eton College', first written in 1742. Other sports popular with Etonians at this time included fives, hoops, marbles, football and kiting.

18*

J.C. Stadler after A. Pugin
Eton Schoolroom
Published by R. Ackermann: London, 1 May 1816
Aquatint 20.1 x 26.5 cms
ETON COLLEGE COLLECTION

Upper School was the large, single schoolroom in which over 170 boys received their various lessons. The masters at Eton were heavily outnumbered by their pupils - in 1834 there were still only nine masters to 570 boys.

19

Unknown Artist
Upper School
Pencil 11.3 x 19 cms
ETON COLLEGE COLLECTION

The master is about to use the birch on an imploring pupil, but when Shelley arrived at Eton discipline was almost non-existent. The drawing seems to be based on the aquatint by Stadler above (entry no. 18).

20
Dr John Keate (1773-1852)
Portrait by Richard Dighton
Signed and inscribed on plate
Etching 23.8 x 19.1 cms
NATIONAL PORTRAIT GALLERY, LONDON

Dr John Keate succeeded Shelley's first headmaster, Dr Joseph Goodall. Unlike his predecessor, 'Flogger' Keate was a fierce disciplinarian, and on one memorable day, 30 June 1832, was said to have flogged, in rapid succession, over 80 boys. He was also known as a thorough and conscientious teacher of the classics.

A near-contemporary of Shelley's at Eton, A.W. Kinglake, has left the following description of Keate:

> He was little more (if more at all) than five feet in height, and he was not very great in girth, but in this space was concentrated the pluck of ten battalions . . . he had the most complete command over his temper - I mean over his *good* temper - which he scarcely ever allowed to appear: you could soon put him out of humour - that is, out of the *ill*-humour which he thought to be fitting for a headmaster. He had a really noble voice, and this he could moderate with great skill, but he had also the power of quacking like an angry duck, and he almost always adopted this mode of communication in order to inspire respect.

Cat. 21

21
Dr John Keate
Portrait by W. Harvey
1828
Pencil, pen and ink 13 x 9.4 cms
ETON COLLEGE COLLECTION

A caricature of Dr. Keate, sketched by one of his more irreverent pupils on the inside cover of his Horace. The tricorn hat was a famous part of the Keate persona.

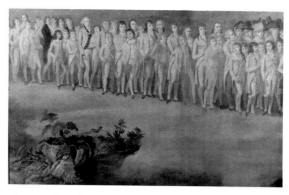

Cat. 22 (detail)

22
R. Livesey (*d.* 1823)
Montem Procession
*c.*1793
Oil on Canvas 135 x 345 cms
ETON COLLEGE COLLECTION

In 1805 Shelley took part in the Ad Montem ceremony at Eton, whereby the whole school would dress up in a variety of splendid costumes and march to the nearby but insignificant Salt Hill. The procession was led by the Captain of the School and the sixth formers, and the junior 'polemen' (so called because of the wands they carried) would bring up the rear. Having reached the summit, everyone would then disperse to collect money by strategically placing themselves (say, on bridges or by local taverns) where they might better extract money, the aim of the collection being to support the Head Boy at university. Meanwhile the 'salt bearers', two senior boys, would stay within the confines of the college and collect fifty guineas from a compliant George III and again from his Queen. The money was presented to the Head Boy.

23
Ad Montem Lists
7 June 1805
ETON COLLEGE COLLECTION

Shelley is recorded as having taken part in the Ad Montem ceremony in 1805 as a corporal. His fellow corporal was Lord Sondes.

24*
Gradus ad Parnassum
Londini: Pro Societate Stationariorum Impressum, 1802
ETON COLLEGE COLLECTION

'Steps towards Parnassus', a Latin text book used by Shelley at Eton. Inscribed on the title page 'P.B. Shelley, 1806'.

25
An Introduction to the Latin Tongue
Eton: 1802
ETON COLLEGE COLLECTION

The Latin grammar most commonly used in England from the mid-eighteenth century. The accompanying Greek grammar (bound together with this volume) was written in Latin, in accordance with the practice of the time. Shelley's later knowledge of Greek was far in advance of that of most men of his day.

26*
Speeches Programme for Election Monday
Eton: Pote & Williams, 1810
ETON COLLEGE COLLECTION

Shelley delivered the fourth Cataline oration by Cicero on Election Monday, 13 July 1810.

ORIGINAL POETRY;

BY

VICTOR AND CAZIRE.

CALL IT NOT VAIN:—THEY DO NOT ERR,

WHO SAY, THAT, WHEN THE POET DIES,

MUTE NATURE MOURNS HER WORSHIPPER.

Lay of the Last Minstrel.

WORTHING:

PRINTED BY C. AND W. PHILLIPS,
FOR THE AUTHORS;
AND SOLD BY J. J. STOCKDALE, 41, PALL-MALL,
AND ALL OTHER BOOKSELLERS.

1810.

27*
Percy Bysshe Shelley and Elizabeth Shelley
Original Poetry by Victor and Cazire
Worthing: C. & W. Phillips, 1810
THE BRITISH LIBRARY BOARD

One of a few surviving copies of Shelley's first publication, a collection of 'terror' narratives and sentimental lyrics written jointly with his sister Elizabeth. It is inscribed: 'Given to me at Eton by the Author Percy Bysshe Shelley, my friend and schoolfellow, 1810. W.W.'. T.J. Wise identifies 'W.W.' as William Wellesley, a son of the Duke of Wellington.

Original Poetry was quickly withdrawn from circulation after the publisher, J.J. Stockdale, realised that it contained, word for word, a poem by M.G. Lewis, the well-known author of *The Monk*'. Shelley blamed 'his co-adjutor' (i.e. his sister) and quickly ordered that all the undistributed copies should be destroyed. The volume's existence was forgotten until 1859, and it was not until 1897 that a copy was finally discovered.

28*
Matthew Gregory 'Monk' Lewis (1775-1818)
Tales of Terror
London: J. Bulmer, 1801
THE BRITISH LIBRARY BOARD

'Monk Lewis's Poems had a great attraction for him,' recalled Shelley's sister Hellen, 'and any tale of spirits, fiends, &c., seemed congenial to his taste at an early age.' *Tales of Terror* was, a particular favourite, and contains the poem, 'Saint Edmund's Eve', that was lifted wholesale for *Original Poetry*. Shelley was to meet its author in 1816, at the Villa Diodati on the shore of Lake Geneva, where Lewis was staying as the guest of Lord Byron (see entry no. 98).

29*
J.J. Stockdale (1770-1847)
Stockdale's Budget, No.1
13 December 1826
THE BRITISH LIBRARY BOARD

In 1826 Shelley's embittered one-time publisher, J.J. Stockdale, sought to group together into a single publication as many of the misdemeanours of the upper-classes as he could muster. Extremely rare, the first number contains Stockdale's account of the plagiarism (intentional or otherwise) that led to the speedy withdrawal of *Original Poetry*.

> Some short time, after the announcement of his poems, I happened to be perusing them, with more attention than I till then had leisure to bestow upon them, when I recognised, in the collection, one which I knew to have been written by Mr. M.G. Lewis, the author of *The Monk*, and I fully anticipated the probable vexation of the juvenile, maiden-author, when I communicated my discovery to Mr. P.B. Shelley.
>
> With all the ardour, incidental to his character, which embraced youthful honour, in all its brilliancy, he expressed the warmest resentment at the imposition practised upon him, by his co-adjutor, and entreated me to destroy all the copies; of which I may say that, through the author and me, about one hundred, on the whole, have been put into circulation. Notwithstanding their comparative demerits, this information may give them value, in the eyes of their possessors, and must have the charm of novelty, perhaps, to all my readers.

30*
Percy Bysshe Shelley
Zastrozzi. A Romance
London: G. Wilkie and J. Robinson, 1810
THE BRITISH LIBRARY BOARD

ZASTROZZI,

A ROMANCE.

BY

P. B. S.

——That their God
May prove their foe, and with repenting hand
Abolish his own works—This would surpass
Common revenge.

PARADISE LOST.

LONDON:

PRINTED FOR G. WILKIE AND J. ROBINSON,
57, PATERNOSTER ROW.

1810.

ST. IRVYNE;

OR,

THE ROSICRUCIAN:

A ROMANCE.

BY

A GENTLEMAN
OF THE UNIVERSITY OF OXFORD.

LONDON:

PRINTED FOR J. J. STOCKDALE,
41, PALL MALL.

1811.

Zastrozzi was probably written between March and August, 1809, when Shelley was 16. Two years later he described the work as the product of 'an intellectual sickness', but the linguistic vitality that marks the great poetry is already evident. In a famous passage the evil Matilda murders the heroine, Julia, in spectacular style:

Julia's senses, roused by Matilda's violence, returned, She cast her eyes upwards, with a timid expression of apprehension, and beheld the infuriate Matilda convulsed by fiercest passion, and a blood-stained dagger raised aloft, threatening instant death.

"Die! Detested wretch," exclaimed Matilda, in a paroxysm of rage, as she violently attempted to bathe the stilletto in the life-blood of her rival; but Julia starting aside, the weapon slightly wounded her neck, and the ensanguined stream stained her alabaster bosom. She fell on the floor, but suddenly starting up, attempted to escape her bloodthirsty persecutor. Nerved anew by this futile attempt to escape her vengeance, the ferocious Matilda seized Julia's floating hair, and holding her back with fiend-like strength, stabbed her in a thousand places; and, with exulting pleasure, again and again buried the dagger to the hilt in her body, even after all remains of life were annihilated.

At last the passions of Matilda, exhausted by their own violence, sank into a deadly calm: she threw the dagger violently from her, and contemplated the terrific scene before her with a sullen gaze.

Before her, in the arms of death, lay him on whom her hopes of happiness seemed to have formed so firm a basis.

31*

Percy Bysshe Shelley
St Irvyne; or, The Rosicrucian: A Romance
London: J.J. Stockdale 1810
THE WORDSWORTH TRUST [THE BRITISH LIBRARY BOARD]

Shelley's second and last gothic novel was probably written between the autumn of 1809 and the spring of 1810, and was published under the anonymous authorship of 'A Gentleman of the University of Oxford'. Copies were distributed to Oxford acquaintances, relatives in Sussex, and to his future wife, the fifteen year-old Harriet Westbrook.

Cat. 32

32*
Joseph Farington
View of High-Street in Oxford
1 June 1793
Aquatint 19.7 x 30.4 cms
JONATHAN WORDSWORTH COLLECTION

Shelley arrived at University College, Oxford in
October 1810, and was at once disappointed with the
claustrophobic and intellectually dormant society.
T.J. Hogg, his closest friend at Oxford, recalled his
words after returning from a tutorial:

> They are very dull people here . . . A little man sent for
> me this morning, and told me in an almost inaudible
> whisper that I must read; 'you must read' he said many
> times in his small voice. I answered that I had no
> objection. He persisted. . . . 'Must I read Euclid?' I asked
> sorrowfully. 'Yes, certainly; and when you've read the
> Greek works I've mentioned, you must begin Aristotle's
> Ethics; and then you may go on to his other treatises. It
> is of the utmost importance to be well-acquainted with
> Aristotle. This he repeated so often that I was quite
> tired, and at last I said 'Must I care about Aristotle? What
> if I do not mind Aristotle?' I then left him, for he seemed
> to be in great perplexity.

33
J. Bluck after William Turner of Oxford
*A View of Oxford from the Gallery in the
Observatory*
Published R. Ackermann: London, 1 July 1814
Etching and aquatint 21 x 28.3 cms
PRIVATE COLLECTION

The frontispiece to Ackermann's *A History of the
University of Oxford its Colleges, Halls and Public
Buildings* (Vol II). Turner has dramatised a
straightforward view of the Oxford skyline by the
use of directional lighting and strongly emphasised
lines of trees.

34*
Percy Bysshe Shelley and T. J. Hogg
Posthumous Fragments of Margaret Nicholson
Oxford: J. Munday, 1810
THE BRITISH LIBRARY BOARD

POSTHUMOUS FRAGMENTS

OF

MARGARET NICHOLSON;

BEING POEMS FOUND AMONGST THE PAPERS OF THAT
NOTED FEMALE WHO ATTEMPTED THE LIFE
OF THE KING IN 1786.

EDITED BY

JOHN FITZVICTOR.

OXFORD:

PRINTED AND SOLD BY J. MUNDAY.

1810.

This pamphlet of burlesque poetry was written in
October and November 1810 and was humourously
attributed to Margaret Nicholson, a mad
washerwoman who had attempted to stab George III
in 1786. This was, perhaps, a precautionary measure,
as several of the poems have strongly Republican
sympathies, and contain veiled attacks on George III
and his ministers. This is one of only two copies
surviving in the original condition.

35*
Percy Bysshe Shelley and T.J. Hogg
The Necessity of Atheism
Worthing: C. & W. Phillips, 1811
THE BRITISH LIBRARY BOARD

One of the two or three surviving perfect copies of
the publication that led to Shelley's and Hogg's
expulsion from Oxford. Knowledge of God's
existence, it argues, can only come from three sources:
from the senses, from reason, and from the testimony
of others. It then proceed to deny the validity of each
of these proofs, and conclude:

> Truth has always been found to promote the best
> interests of mankind. Every reflecting mind must allow
> that there is no proof of the existence of a Deity. Q.E.D.

36*
Minute Book, University College, Oxford,
25 March 1811
Photograph of manuscript
UNIVERSITY COLLEGE, OXFORD

THE

NECESSITY

OF

A T H E I S M.

═══════

Quod clarâ et perspicuâ demonstratione careat
pro vero habere mens omnino nequit humana.

Bacon de Augment. Scient.

═══════

WORTHING:
PRINTED BY C. & W. PHILLIPS:
SOLD IN LONDON AND OXFORD.

The minute reads:

At a meeting of the masters and Fellows held this day it was determined that Thomas Jefferson Hogg and Percy Bysshe Shelley, commoners, be publicly expelled for contumaciously refusing to answer questions proposed to them and for also repeatedly declining to disavow a publication entitled 'The Necessity of Atheism'.

37*
C.J. Ridley
Account of Shelley's expulsion
Photograph of manuscript
UNIVERSITY COLLEGE, OXFORD

Ridley was an undergraduate with Shelley, and later a fellow of University College.

It was announced one morning at a breakfast party, towards the end of Lent Term 1810, that P.B. Shelley who had recently become a member of Univ. Coll. was to be called before the meeting of the Common Room, for being the supposed author of a pamphlet entitled the Necessity of Atheism. This anonymous work, consisting of not many pages, had been studiously sent to most of the dignitaries of the University and to others more or less connected with Oxford. The meeting took place the same day and it was understood that the pamphlet, together with some notes sent with it in which the supposed author's handwriting appeared identified with that of P.B.S. was placed before him. He was asked if he could or would deny the obnoxious production as his.

No direct reply was given either in the affirmative or negative. Shelley having quitted the room T.J. Hogg immediately appeared, voluntarily on his part, to state, that if Shelley had anything to do with it, he (Hogg) was equally implicated, & desired his share of the penalty whatever was inflicted. It has always been supposed that T.J.H. composed the preface. Towards the afternoon, a larger paper bearing the College seal and signed by the Master *and Dean* was affixed to the Hall door, declaring that the two offenders were publicly expelled from the College *for Contumacy in refusing to answer certain questions put to them.* The aforesaid two had made themselves as conspicuous as possible by great singularity of dress, and by walking up and down the centre of the quadrangle, as if proud of their anticipated fate. I believe no one regretted their departure; for there are but few, if any, who are not afraid of Shelley's strange and fantastic pranks, and the still stranger opinions he was known to entertain, but all acknowledged him to be very good humoured and of kind disposition. T.J. Hogg had intellectual powers to a great extent, but unfortunately misdirected. He was most unpopular.

Radical Shelley: 1811-1814

The years following Shelley's expulsion from Oxford up until his meeting with Mary Godwin in 1814 were of a wandering and experimental nature. Four months after leaving Oxford he eloped with Harriet Westbrook, marrying her in Edinburgh on 29 August, against his father's wishes. After a short spell in York he then moved to Keswick, in the English Lake District. During his time at Keswick Shelley was a guest at the northern home of the Duke of Norfolk, Greystoke Castle, and the Duke introduced him to William Calvert of Windy Brow (the son of the Duke's former agent and a friend of William Wordsworth), then aged forty-one, and curiously described by Shelley as 'old'. For the next two months the Calverts are a kindly support to the Shelleys, and through them Shelley makes the acquaintance of Southey, with whom he has several meetings, each touched by increasing alienation. Shelley's uninhibited conversation did cause social problems for Calvert and Southey, and Calvert's daughter, Mary Stanger, told Canon Rawnsley: 'I remember best the sort of look that came upon my father's and upon Southey's face when he talked, and how I and my brothers were hurried out of the room, lest we should hear the conversation.'

After Shelley was attacked by thieves in Chestnut Cottage on 19 January, the Shelleys seem to have moved to the Calverts' house, Greta Bank, before leaving for Ireland, against both Southey's and Calvert's advice. At Dublin Shelley made his only known speech in public, at the Fishamble Street Theatre, and worked hard to distribute his radical pamphlets. From Ireland he moved restlessly about Britain, spending time in Devon, in North Wales, again in Ireland, and then finally in London.

The writing of this period has a concern for the political and social condition of the country. It is strongly radical in flavour, and almost exclusively in prose (the exceptional work, the long poem *Queen Mab* is at least as exciting for its lengthy prose notes as for its poetry). 'Nothing can be equally well expressed in prose that is not tedious and supererogatory in verse', Shelley later wrote in his preface to *Prometheus Unbound*, and it is significant that it was not until he had, in the words of Mary Shelley, 'poured out all the cherished speculations of his youth', that he turned to the more internal language of poetry.

By 1814, however, he had met Mary Godwin and separated from his first wife. Harriet's subsequent suicide, and his failure to gain custody of their children, forced Shelley to come to terms with private as well as public morality, and out of his exploration of the minutiae that make up the wholeness of things, we detect the beginning of the first great phase as a poet.

Cat. 38

38*
Percy Bysshe Shelley
Letter to Sir Timothy Shelley
Edinburgh, 27 September 1811
THE BRITISH LIBRARY BOARD

Shelley defends his recent elopement and marriage to Harriet Westbrook. His wilful, often aggressive tone shows the independence and force of his convictions, but also a need that his recent actions be understood, and even applauded, by his father, and Sir Timothy's continuing silence soon led Shelley to state his case in more emotional terms: 'I shall take the first opportunity of seeing you', he wrote to him on 15 October from York, 'if *you* will not hear my name *I* will pronounce it. Think not I am an insect whom injuries destroy - Had I money enough I would meet you in London and hollow in your ears Bysshe, Bysshe, Bysshe - aye, Bysshe till you're deaf.'

My dear Father -

You have not condescended to answer either of my letters altho the subject of them was such as demanded at least your acknowledgement of their arrival. I can no longer profess ignorance as to the cause of this silence nor refrain from making remarks as to the cause of it: on the supposition of its bare possibility I offered a few in my last, they were respectful & such as you have no right to be offended with, considering that the event has turned out as my suspicions anticipated. - I am married - this is a circumstance, which you have no right to see

with regret. It ought to be the ambition of a real parent to see his son honorably established. You dare not assert the contrary of my present situation, it is such as the laws of my country sanction, such as the very religion which you profess regards as necessary to the true state of it's votaries. I have availed myself of my civil rights in obtaining to myself the legal sanction of this proceeding, I have neither transgressed custom, policy, nor even received notions of religion, my conduct in this respect will bear the severest scrutiny, nor do I suppose you will find one bold enough in paradox to assert that what I have done is criminal. That I did not consult you on the subject is because you could not have placed yourself in my situation, nor however well calculated you may be to judge in other respects, as I suppose you neither aspire to infallibility or intuition, it would be next to impossible to calculate on the mere question of the taste of another, particularly as your general tastes are diametrically opposed to his - Let us admit even that it is an injury that I have done, let us admit that I have wilfully inflicted pain on you, & no moral considerations can palliate the heinousness of my offence - Father, are you a Christian? it is perhaps too late to appeal to your love for me. I appeal to your duty to the God whose worship you profess, I appeal to the terrors of that day which you believe to seal the doom of mortals, then clothed with immortality. - Father are you a Christian? judge not then lest you be judged. - Remember the forgiveness of injuries which Christians profess and if my crime were even deadlier than parricide, forgiveness is your duty. - What! will you not forgive? How then can your boasted professions of Christianity appear to the world, since if you forgive not you can be no Christian - do not rather these hypocritical assumptions of the Christian character lower you in real virtue beneath the *libertine* atheist, for a moral one would practise what you preach, & quietly put in practise that forgiveness, which all your vauntings cannot make you exert - Forgive then! & let me see that at least your professions do not bely your practise, rather let the world see it for if you fear not God as your judge, this tribunal will sit in judgement on your actions - I have done nothing but what is right {& na}tural, nothing is more co{mmon than} elopements between young {people}. The unforgiving spirit of fathers is now become banished to antiquated farces, & silly novels, you hope perhaps to set the fashion, but I have much hope that the world rather than imitating, would laugh at your precedent. -

But by forgiveness I do not mean that barren exertion which contents itself with saying 'I forgive,' & then sits down contented as having discharged its duty. Nor did Jesus Christ mean this, you must bring forth fruits meet for repentance, you must treat me as a Son, and by the common institutions of society your superfluit[i]es ought to go towards my support. - I have no r[i]ght not to expect it. -

What I have said here which appears severe applies to nothing but your unforgivingness. No Son can be so dutiful so respectful as me, & the above remarks are merely urged as what would be my opinion in case you act differently from that mild character which you have hitherto supported. Adieu. Love to Mother Sisters &c - I remain

Your Aff. dut.

P B Shelley -

[P.S.] Will you be so kind as to send me this quarters due to Edinburgh, Post Office - immediately 50£.

Cat. 49 Robert Southey by Adam Buck

Cat. 57 Peter De Wint, *View of a Harbour*

William Godwin by Northcote (detail)
(By courtesy of the Bodleain Library)

Cat. 11 Mary Wollstonecraft after Opie

Mary Shelley by Easton

39*
The Loyal Toast
February 1798
Photograph 25 x 18.5 cms
THE WORDSWORTH TRUST

A cartoon of the Duke of Norfolk, the Whig peer, proposing a toast to 'our Sovereign's health - the Majesty of the People'. This earned him the disfavour of George III, who stripped him of several offices, but the Duke remained a leading Whig in Sussex, and Sir Bysshe Shelley attained his baronetcy largely through his influence. This, coupled with his radical sympathies made him the natural mediator between Shelley and his father, but he was unsuccessful in bringing about a reconciliation.

40
Philip James De Loutherbourg (1740-1812)
Coach going towards Skiddaw
Engraving 39.5 x 56.5 cms
THE WORDSWORTH TRUST

On 3 or 4 November 1811 Shelley and Harriet left York, and after 'some days incessant travelling' arrived at Keswick. Their departure from York was sudden, as they were escaping from Hogg who, perhaps inspired by Shelley's thoughts of free love, had become enamoured of an unwilling Harriet.

De Loutherbourg shows Bassenthwaite Lake in the distance, and the coach is about to descend into Keswick by way of Chestnut Hill, where Shelley was to live for some three months.

Cat. 41

41*
Unknown artist
Shelley's Cottage, Keswick
Photograph 8 x 14 cms
THE WORDSWORTH TRUST

Shelley seems to have arrived at Keswick and taken lodgings with Daniel Crosthwaite, son of Peter, the well-known Keswick museum keeper and Aeolian Harp manufacturer. By 11 November the Shelleys had moved to Chestnut Hill, to the cottage adjoining Mr Gideon Dare's house (spelt 'Dayer's' by Shelley).

The poet's nocturnal activities in general and scientific explorations in particular quickly led to a falling-out with his landlord. On 26 November 1811 he wrote to Elizabeth Hitchener:

> The other night I was explaining to Harriet and Eliza the nature of the atmosphere, and to illustrate my theory I made some experiments on hydrogen gas, one of it's constituent parts. - This was in the garden, and the vivid flame was seen at some distance. - A few days after Mr. Dare entered our cottage and said he had something to say to me. 'Why Sir,' said he, 'I am not satisfied with you. I wish you to leave my house.' - Why Sir? 'Because the country talks very strangely of your proceedings - Odd things have been seen at night near your dwelling I am very ill satisfied with this - Sir I dont like to talk of it. I wish you to provide yourself elsewhere.' - I have with much difficulty quieted Mr. D's fears; he does not however much like us, and I am by no means certain that he will permit us to remain.

42*
Report in the *Cumberland Pacquet*
28 January 1812
Photograph
THE WORDSWORTH TRUST

The paper reports on an attack made on Shelley at Chestnut Cottage:

> Several attempts at robbery have been made within the last fortnight, at Keswick, and in its neighbourhood; but, fortunately, without effect. One of the most remarkable was about seven o'clock, on the night of Sunday the 19th inst. at Chestnut Hill, near Keswick, the seat of GIDEON DARE, Esq. - A part of the house, it seems, is occupied by Mr. SHELLEY and his family. - Mr. Shelley, being alarmed by an unusual noise, (but not knowing, or suspecting, the cause) went to the door; was knocked down by some ruffians, and had remained senseless for a time, when Mr. DARE, hearing the disturbance, rushed out of the house. The villains, no doubt perceiving that he was armed, fled immediately. It could not be ascertained how many the gang consisted of; but the attack was of a very formidable nature, and must stimulate the magistrates and inhabitants of the vicinity to make the most speedy exertions, and adopt the most effectual measures for the security of the town and neighbourhood.

43
William Bellers (fl. 1750-1773)
A View of Derwent Water towards Borrodale
17 January 1774
Engraving 36.5 x 51.8 cms
THE WORDSWORTH TRUST

An early view of Derwentwater, probably taken from Castle Head. The lakeland scenery impressed Shelley - 'I have taken a long *solitary* ramble today', he wrote to Elizabeth Hitchener on 23 November 1811, 'These gigantic mountains piled on each other, these waterfalls, these million shaped clouds tinted by the varying colors of innumerable rainbows hanging between yourself and a lake as smooth and dark as a plain of polished jet.'

Cat. 45

44*
Edward Dayes (1763-1804)
Keswick Lake and the Entrance to Borrowdale
1791
Pencil and watercolour 23.3 x 37.1 cms
THE WORDSWORTH TRUST

Dayes was a gifted topographical watercolourist, a teacher, an engraver, a miniaturist and an author. He taught Thomas Girtin and influenced Turner in his early work.

45
William Westall (1781-1850)
View of Greta Hall and Derwent Water
Watercolour 9.2 x 15 cms
THE WORDSWORTH TRUST

Westall was a close friend of Robert Southey (and through him, of Wordsworth and his family). He illustrated several of Southey's works, and, quite separately, published what are arguably the finest aquatints ever done of the Lake District.

46
William Westall
Derwentwater from Applethwaite
c.1820
Watercolour 20.3 x 30 cms
PRIVATE COLLECTION

Applethwaite is to the north of Keswick on the lower slopes of Skiddaw.

47
Percy Bysshe Shelley
Letter to Elizabeth Hitchener
Keswick, 7 January 1812
THE BRITISH LIBRARY BOARD

In 1811 Shelley began a short-lived but intense intellectual friendship with Elizabeth Hitchener, a schoolmistress at Hurstpierpoint and the daughter of a retired Sussex smuggler. Their earnest and voluminous correspondence, with the young radical enjoying his role as self-appointed teacher to the older woman, provides a detailed record of Shelley's character and ideas at this time. Here Shelley recounts a recent meeting with Robert Southey at Keswick, and already there are signs of the quarrel that was to develop between the two men. Shelley also declares his (unrealised) intention to visit Wordsworth and Coleridge.

I have delayed writing to you for two days - I wronged myself more than you. I have been partly unwilling to break in on some writings I am engaged in, partly in depression - believe me with what pleasure I return to you. My dearest friend I have thought of you and this moment am resolved no longer to delay to think *with* you. Do not fear, I shall *not* be poisoned. I am yet but a viper in the egg, they say, I have all the venom but I cannot sting. Besides they shall not get at me, they cannot. I shall refer to Blackstone, he will tell me what points are criminal and what innocent in the eye of the Law. I do not therefore anticipate a prison. I need not tell you I do not fear it. - But yes, I do; it would curtail much of our Harriets happiness, it would excite too vividly your sympathy, and might obviate my performance of many acts of usefulness which if I have liberty

I can effect. - Godwin yet lives, if government at one time could have destroyed any man Godwin would have ceased to be. - Thomas Paine died a natural death - his writings were far more violently in opposition to government than mine perhaps ever will be. I desire to establish on a lasting basis the happiness of human-kind. Popular insurrections and revolutions I look upon with discountenance; if *such things must be* I will take the side of the People, but my reasonings shall endeavor to ward it from the hearts of the Rulers of the Earth, deeply as I detest them. How does Sir Francis Burdett continue to live; certainly if Mr. Percival could have killed him I do believe he indubitably would have done so. - No my dearest friend, fear not that I shall be destroyed; they cannot, they dare not. I do not dispute but they wd. if they could. - Miss Adams, I cannot pardon her for racking you with these fears. - Friend of my soul cast them off. A beam from the house may destroy you. But I live in hopes that it will not. I feel assured that you are at Hurst in safety. If I did not think so, I could defy the Bishops themselves to paint a Hell so red where I would not go to meet you - Harriet has written to you today; she has informed you of our plans - in a month I shall have completed a tale illustrative of the causes of the failure of the French Revolution to benefit human-kind - At the conclusion of that month [February] we think of going to Dublin where I shall print it - in May to receive your visit in Wales 50 miles nearer than Cumberland. - In fact my friend at this Keswick tho the face of the country is lovely the *people* are detestable. The manufacturers with their contamination have crept into the peaceful vale and deformed the loveliness of Nature with human taint. The debauched servants of the great families who resort contribute to the total extinction of morality. Keswick seems more like a suburb of London than a village of Cumberland. Children are frequently found in the River which the unfortunate women employed at the manufactory destroy. Wales is very different and there *you* shall visit us. The distance is somewhat shorter, the scenery quite as beautiful. - Southey says Expediency ought to [be] made the ground of politics but not of morals. I urged that the most fatal error that ever happened in the world was the seperation of political and ethical science, that the former ought to be entirely regulated by the latter, as whatever was a right criterion of action for an individual must be so for a society which was but an assemblage of individuals, 'that politics were morals more comprehensively enforced.' - Southey did not think the reasoning conclusive - he has a very happy knack when truth goes against him of saying, 'Ah! when you are as old as I am you will think with me' - this talent he employed in the above instance. Nothing can well be more weak. If a thing exists there can always be shewn reasons for its existence. If there cannot it still may exist but can never be the subject of mortal faith. You will see in my 'Hubert Cauvin', the name of the tale that I have spoken of, *expediency insincerity, mystery* adherence to which I do not consider the remotest occasions of violence and blood in the French revolution; indeed their fatal effects are to be traced in every one instance of human life where vice and misery enter into the features of the portraiture. - I do not think so highly of Southey as I did - it is to be confessed that to see him in his family, to behold him in his domestic circle he appears in a most amiable light. - I do not mean that he is or can be the great character which once I linked him to. His mind is terribly narrow compared to it - *Once* he

was this character, everything you can conceive of practised virtue. - Now he is corrupted by the world, contaminated by Custom; it rends my heart when I think what he might have been. - Wordsworth & Coleridge I have yet to see. . . .

48
Percy Bysshe Shelley
Letter to Thomas Hitchener
Nantgwillt, 14 May 1812

Shelley's urgent wish was for Elizabeth Hitchener to join his household of women. This has evidently made her father anxious, but Shelley adopts the same confrontational and indignant tone that characterises his letter to his own father above.

Sir

If you have always considered *character* a posession of the first consequence you & I essentially differ. If you think that an admission of your inferiority to the world leaves any corner by which yourself & character may aspire beyond it's reach, we differ there again. In short, to be candid, I am deceived in my conception of your character. -

I had some difficulty in stifling an indignant surprise on reading the sentence of your letter in which you refuse my invitation to your daughter. How are you entitled to do this? who made you her governor? did you receive this refusal from her to communicate to me? No you have not. - How are *you* then constituted to answer a question which can only be addressed to *her*? believe me such an assumption is as impotent as it is immoral, you may cause your daughter much anxiety many troubles, you may stretch her on a bed of sickness, you may destroy her body, but you are defied to shake her mind. - She is now very ill. *You* have agitated her mind until her frame is seriously deranged - take care Sir, you may destroy her by disease, but her mind is free, *that* you cannot hurt. - Your ideas of *Propriety* (or to express myself clearer, of *morals*) are all founded on considerations of *profit*. I do not mean money but profit in its extended sense: - As to your daughter's welfare on that *she* is competent to judge or at least she alone has a right to decide. With respect to your own comfort you of course do right to consult it, that she has done so you ought to be more grateful than you appear. - But how can you demand as a right what has been generously conceded as a favor; you do right to consult your own comfort, but the whole world besides may surely be excused.

Neither the laws of Nature, nor of England have made children private property. -

Adieu, when next I hear from you, I hope that time will have liberalized your sentiments.
Your's truly
P.B. Shelley

49*
Adam Buck
Robert Southey and His Daughter
1824
Pen and watercolour 40 x 40 cms

Southey is shown with one of his daughters and his son and future biographer, Cuthbert. The castle in the background is St. Michael's Mount, Cornwall, the setting for one of his comic ballads.

Cat. 49

50*
Caroline Bowles (1786-1854)
Front of Greta Hall
Watercolour 22.2 x 20.5 cms
THE WORDSWORTH TRUST

In 1839, after a correspondence stretching back over twenty years, Caroline Bowles became the second Mrs Southey. Her real ambitions were poetic, but she is now valued for her watercolours.

51
Caroline Bowles
View from the window of Southey's study
Watercolour 34.5 x 43 cms
THE WORDSWORTH TRUST

Shelley was permitted into Southey's study, but found that he was not allowed to take down books from the shelves. He concluded that this was because Southey considered their riches to be secret, and for himself alone.

52
Percy Bysshe Shelley
Letter to Robert Southey
Pisa, 17 August 1820
Transcribed by Edith May Southey
THE BRITISH LIBRARY BOARD

Eight years after leaving Keswick, Shelley is replying to Southey's recent accusation: 'have they [your opinions] not brought immediate misery upon others, and guilt, which is all but irremediable, on yourself?'.

Dear Sir

Allow me to acknowledge the sincere pleasure which I received from the first paragraph of your letter. The disavowal it contained was just such as I firmly anticipated.

Allow me also to assure you, that no menace implied in my letter could have the remotest application to yourself. I am not indeed aware that it contained any menace. I recollect expressing what contempt I felt, in the hope that you might meet the wretched hireling who has so closely imitated your style as to deceive all but those who knew you into a belief that he was you, at Murray's, or somewhere, and that you would inflict my letter on him, as a recompense for sowing ill-will between those who wish each other all good, as you and I do.

I confess your recommendation to adopt the system of ideas you call Christianity has little weight with me, whether you mean the popular superstition in all its articles, or some more refined theory with respect to those events and opinions which put an end to the graceful religion of the Greeks. To judge of the doctrines by their effects, one would think that this religion were called the religion of Christ and Charity, *ut lucus a non lucendo*, when I consider the manner in which they seem to have transformed the disposition and understanding of you and men of the most amiable manners and the highest accomplishments, so that even when recommending Christianity you cannot forbear breathing out defiance, against the express words of Christ. What would you have me think? You accuse me, on what evidence I cannot guess, of *guilt* - a bald word, sir, this, and one which would have required me to write to you in another tone, had you addressed it to any one except myself. Instead, therefore, of refraining from 'judging that you be not judged', you not only judge but condemn, and that to a punishment which its victim must be either among the meanest or the loftiest not to regard as bitterer than death. But you are such a pure one as Jesus Christ found not in all Judea to throw the first stone against the woman taken in adultery!

With what care do the most tyrannical Courts of Judicature weigh evidence, and surround the accused with protecting forms; with what reluctance do they pronounce their cruel and presumptuous decisions compared with you! You select a single passage out of a life otherwise not only spotless but spent in an impassioned pursuit of virtue, which looks like a blot, merely because I regulated my domestic arrangements without deferring to the notions of the vulgar, although I might have done so quite as conveniently had I descended to their base thoughts - this you call *guilt*. I might answer you in another manner, but I take God to witness, if such a Being is now regarding both you and me, and I pledge myself if we meet, as perhaps you expect, before Him after death, to repeat the same in His presence - that you accuse me wrongfully. I am innocent of ill, either done or intended; the consequences you allude to flowed in no respect from me. If you were my friend, I could tell you a history that would make you open your eyes; but I shall certainly never make the public my familiar confidant.

You say you judge of opinions by the fruits; so do I, but by their remote and permanent fruits - such fruits of rash judgment as Christianity seems to have produced in you. The immediate fruits of all new opinions are indeed calamity to the promulgators and professors; but we see the end of nothing, and it is in acting well, in contempt of present advantage, that virtue consists.

I need not be instructed that the opinion of the ruling party to which you have attached yourself always exacts, contumeliously receives, and never reciprocates, toleration. 'But there is a tide in the affairs of men' - it is rising while we speak.

Another specimen of your Christianity is the judgment you form of the spirit of my verses, from the abuse of the Reviews. I have desired Mr. Ollier to send you those last published; they may amuse you, for one of them - indeed neither have anything to do with those speculations on which we differ.

I cannot hope that you will be candid enough to feel, or if you feel, to own, that you have done ill in accusing, even in your mind, an innocent and a persecuted man, whose only real offence is the holding opinions something similar to those which you once held respecting the existing state of society. Without this, further correspondence, the object for which I renewed it being once obtained, must, from differences in our judgment, be irksome and useless. I hope some day to meet you in London, and ten minutes' conversation is worth ten folios of writing. Meanwhile assure yourself that, among all your good wishers, you have none who wish you better than, dear sir,
Your very faithful and obedient Servant,
P.B. Shelley.

P.S. - I ought not to omit that I have had sickness enough, and that at this moment I have so severe a pain in the side that I can hardly write. All this is of no account in the favour of what you, or anyone else, calls Christianity; surely it would be better to wish me health and healthful sensations. *I* hope the chickens will not come home to roost!

53
Robert Southey (1774-1843)
Letter to Percy Bysshe Shelley
Keswick, 12 October 1820
Transcribed by Edith May Southey
THE BRITISH LIBRARY BOARD

Southey's response takes a high moral stance. It severely recalls Shelley's separation from Harriet ('ask your own heart, whether you have not been the whole, sole, and direct cause of her destruction'), recommends him to consider Christianity, and discourages all further correspondence. 'I saw Southey's reply', recalled Thomas Medwin, 'which alluded to something that passed at Keswick when Shelley was there with his first wife whose fate was so appalling - the letter affected Shelley deeply'.

Yesterday, sir, I received your present of the Cenci and the Prometheus. I thank you for these books, and little as the time is which I can allow for correspondence of any kind, I think it proper to [reply to ?] your letter or August 29th [sic], which announced them.

You tell me that I have selected out of a life 'otherwise not only spotless but spent in an impassioned pursuit of virtue, a single passage which looks like a blot, merely because you regulated your domestic arrangements without reference to the notions of the vulgar', and you accuse me of passing a rash and unjust judgment. Let us look to the case - I will state it with no uncharitable spirit, and with no unfriendly purpose.

When you were a mere youth at College you took up atheistical opinions - you endeavoured to make proselytes to these opinions in a girls' boarding-school. One of the girls was expelled for the zeal with which she entered into your views, and you made her the most honourable amends in your power by marrying her. Shortly afterwards you came to Keswick. There was no appearance, when I saw you, that your principles had injured your heart. As yet you had had no proof of this tendency in yourself, but you had seen a memorable one in the conduct of your first speculation (speculative?) and literary associate, who accompanied you to Scotland on your matrimonial expedition, and on your way back would have seduced your wife. This I had from your own lips: your feelings at that time were humane and generous, and your intentions good. I felt a greater interest in your welfare than I expressed to you, and took such indirect means as were in my power of assuring your father that, erroneous as your conduct was, it was still to be expected that your heart would bring you right, and that everything might be hoped from your genius and your virtues.

Such was my opinion of you when we parted. What I heard of your subsequent conduct tended always to lower it, except as regarded your talents. At length you forsook your wife, because you were tired of her, and had found another woman more suited to your taste. You could tell me a history, you say, which would make me open my eyes: perhaps they are already open. It is a matter of public notoriety that your wife destroyed herself. Knowing in what manner she bore your desertion, I never attributed this to her sensibility on that score. I have heard it otherwise explained: I have heard that she followed your example as faithfully as your lessons, and that the catastrophe was produced by shame. Be this as it may, ask your own heart, whether you have not been the whole, sole, and direct cause of her destruction. You corrupted her opinions; you robbed her of her moral and religious principles; you debauched her mind. But for you and your lessons she might have gone through the world innocently and happily.

I will do you justice, sir. While you were at Keswick you told your bride that you regarded marriage as a mere ceremony, and would live with her no longer than you liked her. I dare say you told her this before the ceremony, and that you persuaded her that there was nothing sacred in the tie. But that she should have considered this as the condition upon which she was married, or that you yourself at that time looked forward to a breach of the connexion, I do not believe. I think still too well of your original nature to believe it. She trusted to your heart, not your opinions. She relied upon your generosity, your affection, your tenderness, your first love. The wife of your youth might well rely upon these, and with the more confidence when she became the mother of your first children.

No, sir, you were not depraved enough to think you could ever desert her when you talked of it as a possible event; and if you had not tampered with your own heart with speculations upon such possibilities, and contemplating them as lawful and allowable, her confidence in you could not have been deceived. That sophistry which endeavours to confound the plain broad distinction between right and wrong can never be employed innocently or with impunity. Some men are wicked by disposition, others become so in their weakness, yielding to temptation; but you have corrupted in yourself an excellent nature. You have sought for temptation and courted it; you have reasoned yourself into a state of mind so pernicious that your character, with your domestic arrangements, as you term it, might

A Poet Mounted as the Court-Pegasus (1817)

Cat. 55

furnish the subject for the drama more instructive, and scarcely less painful, than the detestable story of the Cenci, and this has proceeded directly from your principles. . . . It is the Atheist's Tragedy. You might have regulated your domestic arrangements, you say, quite as conveniently to yourself if you had descended to the base thoughts of the vulgar. I suppose this means that you might have annulled your marriage as having been contracted during your minority. You say that your only real crime is the holding opinions something similar to those which I once held respecting the existing state of society. That, sir, is not your crime, it would only be your error; your offence is moral as well as political, practical as well as speculative. Nor were my opinions ever similar to yours in any other point than that, desiring, as I still desire, a greater equality in the condition of men, I entertained erroneous notions concerning the nature of that improvement in society, and the means whereby it was to be promoted. Except in this light, light and darkness are not more opposite than my youthful opinions and yours. You would have found me as strongly opposed in my youth to Atheism and immorality of any kind as I am now, and to that abominable philosophy which teaches self-indulgence instead of self-control.

The Christianity which I recommended to your consideration is to be found in the Scriptures and in the Book of Common Prayer. I would fain have had you to believe that there is judgment after death, and to learn, and understand, and feel all sins may be forgiven through the merits and mediation of Jesus Christ. You mistake my meaning when you suppose that I wished you to be afflicted with bodily suffering: but I repeat, that any affliction which might bring you to better mind would be a dispensation of mercy. And here, sir, our correspondence must end. I never should have sought it; but having been led into it, it appeared to me a duty to take that opportunity of representing you to yourself as you appear to me, with little hope indeed of producing any good effect, and yet not altogether hopeless; for though

you may go on with an unawakened mind, a seared conscience, and a hardened heart, there will be seasons of misgivings, when that most sacred faculty which you have laboured to destroy makes itself felt. At such times you may remember me as an earnest monitor whom you cannot suspect of ill-will, and whom it is not in your power to despise, however much you may wish to repel his administrations with contempt.
Believe me, sir, your sincere well-wisher,
Robert Southey.

54*
Lord Byron
The Vision of Judgement
7 May 1821
JOHN MURRAY COLLECTION

Byron's poem, first published in *The Liberal* in 1822, is a parody of Southey's own *A Vision of Judgement*. Here, Byron characterises Southey as the contradictory and hypocritical poet:

> He had sung against all battles, and again
>   In their high praise and glory; he had call'd
> Reviewing "the ungentle craft," and then
>   Become as base a critic as ere crawl'd -
> Fed, paid, and pamper'd by the very men
>   By whom his muse and morals had been maul'd:
> He had written much blank verse, and blanker prose,
>   And more of both than any body knows.
>
> He had written Wesley's life: - here, turning round
>   To Sathan, "Sir, I'm ready to write yours,
> "In two octavo volumes, nicely bound,
>   "With notes and preface, all that most allures
> "The pious purchaser; and there's no ground
>   "For fear, for I can choose my own reviewers:
> "So let me have the proper documents,
>   "That I may add you to my other saints."

55*
Unknown artist
A Noble Poet - Scratching up his Ideas
Published by J. Johnston, London 1 January 1823
Photograph 29.4 x 23.5 cms
THE WORDSWORTH TRUST

Cat. 57

Byron is shown with a devil crouched on his head, a clear reference to Southey's characterization of the Shelley-Byron-Leigh Hunt school as 'Satanic'. In his preface to *A Vision of Judgement* Southey wrote:

> The school which they have set up may be properly called the Satanic school; for though their productions breathe the spirit of Belial in their lascivious parts, and the spirit of Molloch in those loathsome images of atrocities and horrors which they delight to represent, they are more especially characterised by a Satanic spirit of pride and audacious impiety, which still betrays their wretched feelings of hopelessness wherewith it is allied.

To Byron's right are copies of *The Vision of Judgement*, *Heaven and Earth*, and *The Liberal*. Above the desk is a picture of Cain killing Abel, a reference to Byron's play *Cain*. The paper on which he is writing is headed 'Il Liberale'. *The Liberal* was a radical magazine started by Leigh Hunt in 1822, The first number contained *The Vision of Judgement* and Shelley's translation of the May-day night scene in Goethe's *Faust*. The political standpoint of the print is Tory; compare it to the one of Southey to the left.

56

Thomas De Quincey (1785-1859)
Portrait by James Archer
Pencil 33 x 26 cms
THE WORDSWORTH TRUST

Although he was then living in nearby Grasmere, Thomas De Quincey never met Shelley. He later wrote:

> Some neighbourly advantages I might certainly have placed at Shelley's disposal: Grasmere, for instance, itself, which tempted at that time by a beauty that had not *then* been sullied; Wordsworth, who then lived at Grasmere; Elleray and Professor Wilson, nine miles further; finally, my own library, which, being rich in the wickedest of German speculations, would naturally have been more to Shelley's taste than the Spanish library of Southey.'

Shelley however was to be very attracted to Spanish works, especially the drama of Calderon.

57

Peter De Wint (1784-1849)
View of a Harbour
c.1830
Watercolour 25 x 63 cms
THE LAING ART GALLERY, NEWCASTLE UPON TYNE

De Wint's marvellous watercolour shows a view of Whitehaven, the port from which Shelley sailed to Dublin after leaving Keswick, February 1812. De Wint was to become an acquaintance of Keats, and contributed to help the young poet sail to Italy in 1820 in search of health.

58

William Daniell (1769-1837)
Whitehaven, Cumberland
1 April 1816
Aquatint 16.7 x 24 cms
PRIVATE COLLECTION

William Daniell, the brother-in-law of William Westall, was a skilled watercolourist and superb aquatinter. Between 1813 and 1823 he was occupied with his *Voyage Round Great Britain*.

59*

Percy Bysshe Shelley
Letter to Elizabeth Hitchener
Whitehaven, 3 February 1812
THE BRITISH LIBRARY BOARD

Writing from Whitehaven, just before his departure for Ireland, Shelley describes his disillusionment with Southey, and praises his friends the Calverts.

> My dearest Friend
>   We are now at Whitehaven, which is a miserable manufacturing seaport Town. I write to you a short letter to inform you of our safety, and that the wind which will fill the sails of our packet tonight is favorable and fresh. - Certainly it is laden with some of your benedictions or with the breath of the disembodied

Cat. 60

Cat. 61

virtuous who smile upon our attempt. - We set off tonight at 12 oClock and arrive at the Isle of Man whence you will hear from us, tomorrow morning. Thence we proceed when the wind serves to Dublin. - We may be detained some days in the Island, if the weather is fine we shall not regret it. At all events we shall escape this filthy town and horrible Inn. - Now do you not think of us with other feelings than those of hope and confidence. I know that belief is not a voluntary action of the mind, but I think your confidence would not be groundless. To give you an idea of the perfect fearlessness with which Harriet and Eliza accompany my attempt, they think of no inconveniences but those of a wet night and sea-sickness, which in fact we find to be the only real ones. - Assassination either by private or public enemies appear[s] to me to be the phantoms of a mind whose affectionate friendship has outrun the real state of the case. Assure yourself that such things are now super-annuated, & infeasable. Give me, as I have before said, the confidence of your hope the sanguineness of your certainty, joined to that concern for welfare which we mutually felt. For my friend wrong me not by thinking that in this bustle of present events, and enthusiastic anticipation of future, that you are forgotten or unheeded, or lightly remembered. No. *Your* cooperation and presence is wanting to perfect the present, & with the certainty of hope do I conceive of you in future as a friend & dear friend who will form the foreground of the picture which my fancy designs.

We felt regret at leaving Keswick. I passed Southeys house without *one* sting. - He is a man who *may* be amiable in his *private* character stained and false as is his public one. - he *may* be amiable, but if he is my feelings are liars, and I have been so long accustomed to trust to them in these cases that the opinion of the world is not the likeliest criminator to impeach their credibility. But we left the Calverts. I hope some day to shew you *Mrs.* Calvert. I shall not forget her, but will preserve her memory as another flower to compose a garland which I intend to present to *you*. - Assure yourself that it is a

fragrant one, that if it breathes *not* of Heaven, I am an impostor and a silly gardener that picks weeds where roses grow. I confess that I cannot expect you will come to us *now;* if you *do,* if you do, it will be a piece of good fortune for which my mind will be unprepared but which it will hail with more delight than the Magi did 'the dayspring from on high.' - But in the Summer when you come to us if you again depart, I shall say 'you are the deaf adder that stoppeth her ears, and hearkneth not to the voice of the Charmer.' I stop the wheels of the former sentence for a minute just to say, that I do not even allegorize myself by the 'Charmer.' - I entreat you, do not allow the ingratitude of that little viper Anne to disturb you. - Nor think it a{ny}thing like an appearance of *original sin*. - I do not tell you by the former to staunch the beating arteries of your heart of sensibility. - Turn the channel to some better and some greater object, 'The welfare of general man.'- Even sympathise with me in Dublin. - Of the latter I will give you a reason hereafter, indeed I believe that I have given you many already. - Well, adieu. - Harriet and Eliza in excellent spirits bid you an affectionate adieu. - Pray what are you to be *called* when you come to us for Eliza's name is Eliza and Miss Hitchener is too long too broad and too deep.

Adieu.

Your

P B Shelley.

60*
William Calvert (1770-1829)
Portrait by Mary Calvert
c.1803
Pencil sketch 14.8 x 12.5 cms
THE WORDSWORTH TRUST

AN ADDRESS,

TO THE

IRISH PEOPLE,

BY PERCY BYSSHE SHELLEY.

ADVERTISEMENT.

The lowest possible price is set on this publication, because it is the intention of the Author to awaken in the minds of the Irish poor, a knowledge of their real state, summarily pointing out the evils of that state, and suggesting rational means of remedy.—Catholic Emancipation, and a Repeal of the Union Act, (the latter, the most successful engine that England ever wielded over the misery of fallen Ireland,) being treated of in the following address, as grievances which unanimity and resolution may remove, and associations conducted with peaceable firmness, being earnestly recommended, as means for embodying that unanimity and firmness, which must finally be successful.

Dublin:
1812.

Price—5d.

William Calvert was an elder brother of Raisley, Wordsworth's schoolfellow at Hawkshead School who, dying aged 21, in 1795 bequeathed £900 of his estate to the poet. The previous year, the Calverts had lent William and Dorothy rooms in their farmhouse at Windy Brow. By the time of his marriage to Mary Mitchinson in 1801, William Calvert had built himself a new house (with a chemical laboratory) just beside Windy Brow, naming it 'Greta Bank'. Despite De Quincey's claim (in a review of Gilfillan's Literary Portraits 1845-6) that Southey first called on Shelley when he arrived at Keswick, H.D. Rawnsley in his *The Last of the Calverts* (Cornhill Magazine 1890) seems correct in asserting that the poets met at Greta Bank in December 1811.

61*
Mary Calvert (1776-1834)
Portrait by unknown artist
Pencil and watercolour
H 12.5 cms
THE WORDSWORTH TRUST

Of Mrs Calvert, who alone seems to have not disapproved of his going to Ireland, Shelley wrote to Elizabeth Hitchener:

'I hope some day to show you *Mrs. Calvert. I* shall not forget her, but will preserve her memory as another flower to compose a garland which I intend to present to *you.* - Assure yourself that it is a fragrant one, that if it breathes *not* of Heaven, I am an imposter and a silly gardner that picks weeds where roses grow.'

62*
Percy Bysshe Shelley
An Address to the Irish People
Dublin: 1812
THE BRITISH LIBRARY BOARD

In this pamphlet, written at Keswick, Shelley forwards the cause of Catholic emancipation in Ireland and argues for the repeal of the Act of Union. On 26 January 1812 he wrote to Elizabeth Hitchener: 'It is intended to familiarize to uneducated apprehensions ideas of liberty, benevolence, peace and toleration.' Shelley arrived in Ireland on the 12th of February and in a month had distributed all 1,500 copies of the pamphlet. In Ireland he met J.P. Curran, the Irish political leader, and on 28 Febraury made one long and not entirely successful speech at Fishamble Street, Dublin, at an open meeting organised by the Catholic Committee. His contacts included friends of Godwin such as Curran, and former radicals of the United Irishmen such as the intrepid campaigner Archibald Hamilton Rowan. Shelley used the matter of his *Address to the Irish People* as the substance of his speech. His reward was to be noticed by the two government spies in the audience. Somewhat discouraged, Shelley and Harriet left Dublin on 4 April, with their Irish servant Dan Healy.

63
Miscellanies of the Philobiblion Society (Vol. XII)
London: Whittingham and Wilkins, 1868-9
THE BRITISH LIBRARY BOARD

The volume contains a reprint of Shelley's *A Declaration of Rights*, composed in Dublin in the spring of 1812 as a broadside to be posted on the walls of public buildings in the city. It is a summation of the republican creed, indebted to two French Declarations of Rights - that adopted by the Constituent Assembly in August 1789, and that proposed by Robespierre in April, 1793. It is also indebted to Thomas Paine, whose *Rights of Man* was published in 1792. After returning to England, Shelley determined to post his broadside on the walls of Barnstaple, and his Irish servant Daniel Healy was arrested while attempting to distribute it. By this time Shelley's activities were being closely watched by government agents, and on the 19th of August, the day Daniel Healy was arrested, Henry Drake, town clerk of Barnstaple, wrote to the Home Secretary, Lord Sidmouth:

Last evening a Man was observed distributing and posting some Papers about this Town intitled "Declaration of Rights" and on being apprehended and brought before the Mayor, stated his name to be Daniel Hill, and that he is a servant to P.B. Shelley Esq. now residing at Hoopers Lodgings at Lymouth near Linton a small village bordering on the Bristol Channel and about 17 miles from Barnstaple. ... On interrogating Hill, more particularly respecting his Master, he said he principally lived in London but in what Part of it he did not know, but that he had lived with him in Sackville Street that he married a Miss Westbrooke or Westbrooks, a Daughter of Mr Westbrooke of Chapel Street Grosvenor Square and that two sisters of Mrs Shelley are now with her at Lymouth, and Mr Shelley his Master's Father is a member of Parliament. This is all the Information the Mayor could get from Hill, but he is being informed that Mr. Shelley is being regarded with suspicious eyes since he has been at Lymouth, from the Circumstances of his very extensive correspondence, and many of his Packages and Letters being addressed to Sir Francis Burdett and it is also said that Mr. Shelley has sent off so many as 16 Letters by the same Post The Mayor has also been informed that Mr. Shelley has been seen frequently to go out in a Boat a short distance from Land and drop some Bottles into the Sea, and that at one time he was observed to wade into the Water and drop a Bottle which afterwards drifting ashore was picked up, and on being broken was found to contain a seditious Paper, Contents of which the Mayor has not yet been able to ascertain but will apprize your Lordship immediately on learning further particulars.

This correspondence, addressed directly to the Home Secretary, shows the seriousness with which Shelley's activities were taken, and the authorities' general alarm at the general situation in England at the time. Sidmouth's vast network of government spies and informers was one of the most extensive ever to be organised.

Cat. 64

64*
William Daniell
Lynmouth on the coast of North Devon
Published 1 July 1814
Engraving 16.2 x 24 cms
PRIVATE COLLECTION

Shelley, Harriet Shelley and her sister Eliza arrived at Lynmouth on 28 June 1812, and were soon joined there by Elizabeth Hitchener. It was remote place,

cut off from usual communications, but Shelley found new ways to distribute his pamphlets; he not only threw them into the sea in bottles, but also launched them on miniature boats, and even fastened them to home-made fire balloons. At the same time he began his long, ambitious poem *Queen Mab*.

QUEEN MAB;

A

PHILOSOPHICAL POEM:

WITH NOTES.

BY

PERCY BYSSHE SHELLEY.

ECRASEZ L'INFAME!
Correspondance de Voltaire.

Avia Pieridum peragro loca, nullius ante
Trita solo ; juvat integros accedere fonteis ;
Atque haurire : juratque novos decerpere flores.
*   *   *   *   *
Unde prius nulli velarint tempora musæ.
Primum quod magnis doceo de rebus ; et arctis
Religionum animos nodis exsolvere pergu.
Lucret. lib. iv.

Δοι τυ τῦ, καὶ κοσμον κινησω.
Archimedes.

LONDON:
PRINTED BY P. B. SHELLEY,
23, Chapel Street, Grosvenor Square.
1813.

65*
Percy Bysshe Shelley
Queen Mab; A Philosophical Poem: With Notes
London: P.B. Shelley, 1813
THE BRITISH LIBRARY BOARD

This is the copy Shelley used when transforming a portion of the poem into a new work, *The Daemon of the World*. The whole of the first two cantos are revised, altered and interlined in Shelley's hand. It is unusual in that it retains the incriminating title page, where Shelley has acknowledged himself to be the printer. Shelley wrote from Dublin to Thomas Hookham, March 1813: 'The notes will be long philosophical, & Anti Christian - this will be unnoticed in a Note.' Shelley's confidence was misplaced, for the notes especially gave the poem a currency in pirated editions through the next fifty years. The book is printed as Shelley demanded: 'Let only 250 copies be printed. A small neat Quarto on fine paper & so to catch the aristocrats: They will not read it but their sons & daughters may'. Only 70 copies were in fact distributed, for Shelley himself feared the poem was imprudently radical.

66*
Percy Bysshe Shelley
Queen Mab
London: Joint Stock Book Company, 1826
THE WORDSWORTH TRUST

Queen Mab was the most widely-read of Shelley's poems, mostly through cheap, pirated editions such as this. At least 14 separate editions of the poem were published between 1821 and 1845.

67*
Percy Bysshe Shelley
A Refutation of Deism
London: Schulze and Dean, 1814
THE BRITISH LIBRARY BOARD

Probably composed between 1812 and 1813, while the poet was writing *Queen Mab*. It aims to prove that deism, the prevailing philosophical religion of the time, is untenable. Shelley knew he would risk prosecution if he published his ideas in the bold manner of *Queen Mab*. Hence he expressed them in the form of a dialogue between Theosophus, a deist, and Eusebes, a christian. Shelley's approach, even in his best poetry, has an element of debate: his stance is one of reasonableness, his conclusion is delicate in its fence-sitting. Thus, Theosophus gives up deism and declares a preference - not for Christianity, but for 'so much of the christian scheme as is consistent with any persuasion of goodness, unity, and majesty of God.'

A

REFUTATION

OF

DEISM:

IN

A DIALOGUE.

———

ΣΥΝΕΤΟΙΣΙΝ.

════════════

London:

PRINTED BY SCHULZE AND DEAN,

13, POLAND STREET.

———

1814.

Poetry and Travel: 1814-16

Shelley met Mary Godwin at her father's house in May 1814. 'Nothing that I ever read in tale or history could present a more striking image of a sudden, violent, irresistable, uncontrollable passion' wrote Thomas Love Peacock in his *Memoir* of the poet, and by June they had eloped to the Continent, accompanied by Mary's step-sister Claire Clairmont (who acted as interpreter). Their trip, a six-week dash through France, Switzerland and Germany, was later recounted by Mary in the *History of a Six Weeks' Tour* (1817).

The *History of a Six Weeks' Tour* also included the first publication of Shelley's great poem *Mont Blanc*, written after a further visit to Switzerland in 1816, this time as neighbour to Lord Byron on the shores of Lake Geneva. It was Shelley's first meeting with Byron, who was then composing Canto III of *Childe Harold*, and his judgements were reserved. 'Lord Byron is an exceedingly interesting person' he wrote to Peacock, 'and as such is it not to be regretted that he is the slave to the vilest and most vulgar prejudices, and as mad as the winds'. Two years later, on 18 December 1818 he wrote again to Peacock: 'I entirely agree with what you say about Childe Harold. The spirit in which it is written is, if insane, the most wicked & mischievous insanity that was ever given forth. It is a kind of obstinate & selfwilled folly in which he hardens himself. I remonstrated with him in vain on the tone of mind from which such a view of things alone arises.' But as the friendship developed, so its benefits became clear. Shelley was to learn from Byron a vital satiric voice, and, following their meeting in Geneva, a new directness, conversational in tone, can be felt in his poetry. At the same time Byron's development as a poet from *Childe Harold* to *Don Juan* owed something to Shelley's influence. 'It may be vanity', Shelley wrote to Mary on 10 August 1821 after reading part of *Don Juan*, 'but I think I see the trace of my earnest exhortations to him to create something wholly new.'

One evening, 17 June 1816, whilst the Shelleys were visiting Byron at the Villa Diodati, to the south-east of Geneva, the idea arose of writing, in friendly competition, a collection of ghost tales. '. . . it proved a wet, uncongenial summer', wrote Mary Shelley in her introduction to *Frankenstein*, 'and incessant rain often confined us for days to the house. Some volumes of ghost stories, translated from the German into French, fell into our hands. . . . "We will each write a ghost story," said Lord Byron; and his proposition was acceded to.' This was to result in a fragment by Byron (published in 1819 against his wishes with his *Mazeppa*) on the theme of the vampire - a theme later appropriated by Polidori, Byron's personal physician, in his novel *The Vampyre* (1819). The Polidori work that came out of 17 June was *Ernestus Berchtold, or the Modern Oedipus*. More famously, it produced *Frankenstein, or the Modern Prometheus* by Mary Shelley.

68*
Mary Wollstonecraft Shelley (1797-1851)
Portrait by Richard Rothwell
*c.*1840
Photograph 50 x 40 cms
THE WORDSWORTH TRUST

The portrait, which was exhibited by the artist in 1840, shows Mary in middle-age, nearly twenty years after Shelley's death. It hung above the mantlepiece in the place of honour in the Shelley 'sanctum' at Boscombe Manor.

HISTORY

OF

A SIX WEEKS' TOUR

THROUGH

A PART OF FRANCE,
SWITZERLAND, GERMANY, AND HOLLAND:

WITH LETTERS

DESCRIPTIVE OF

A SAIL ROUND THE LAKE OF GENEVA, AND OF
THE GLACIERS OF CHAMOUNI.

LONDON:

PUBLISHED BY T. HOOKHAM, JUN.
OLD BOND STREET;

AND C. AND J. OLLIER,
WELBECK STREET.

1817.

69*
Percy Bysshe Shelley and Mary Shelley
History of A Six Weeks' Tour
London: T. Hookham, Jun., and C. & J. Ollier, 1817
THE BRITISH LIBRARY BOARD

An account that draws upon two visits to the continent: first the elopement trip of Shelley, Mary Shelley and Claire Clairmont through France, Switzerland, Germany and Holland from July to September 1814, and second their journey through France to Geneva and Savoy in 1816. It includes the first publication of *Mont Blanc*.

70
David Roberts (1796-1864)
Abbéville
Watercolour 30.5 x 22 cms
ETON COLLEGE COLLECTION

Abbéville was one of the first stops on the elopement trip with Mary Shelley. 'We travelled all day,' writes Shelley in Mary Shelley's journal for 31 July 1814, 'and arrived at 2 in the morning at Abbéville, where we slept.' The previous day Mrs Godwin, who had followed Shelley, Mary and Claire across the Channel, left France, having been unsuccessful in persuading her daughter Claire to return with her.

Cat. 71

71*
E. Finden (1791-1857) after W. Purser
Diodati. The Residence of Lord Byron
Published by John Murray, London 1833
Engraving 8 x 12 cms
IAIN BAIN COLLECTION [THE BRITISH LIBRARY BOARD]

The Villa Diodati was Byron's residence in 1816. Lake Geneva lay two hundred yards in front of it, and the Jura mountains could be seen in the distance. The property belonged to Edouard Diodati, a descendant of Milton's friend Charles Diodati. Milton had visited the house in 1639. The Shelleys lived a short walking distance away, at the Maison Chappuis.

72
Lord Byron (1788-1824)
Childe Harold
1816
BARCLAYS BANK PLC

The earliest of three surviving manuscripts of Canto Three, inscribed 'This M.S. was given by Byron to Scrope Davies at Geneva September 2d 1816'. It was found in 1976 amongst the literary papers deposited at a London bank by Byron's friend Scrope Davies in 1820, shortly before gambling debts forced him to flee the country. This material is currently on loan to the British Library.

Cat. 73

73

John William Polidori (1795-1821)
Portrait by F.G. Gainsford
Oil on canvas 58.4 x 48 cms
NATIONAL PORTRAIT GALLERY, LONDON

John William Polidori was the son of a Tuscan emigré and man of letters, Gaetano Polidori, and the uncle of Christina and Dante Gabriel Rosetti. At the age of 21 he was hired by Byron as his travelling physician, and accompanied the poet to Geneva in 1816. Byron's publisher, John Murray, offered Polidori £500 for an account of his tour with Byron, and the subsequent diary contains many interesting anecdotes about Byron and the Shelleys. On the 27th of May 1816 Polidori writes: 'P.S. the author of *Queen Mab*, came; bashful, shy, consumptive; twenty six; separated from his wife; keeps the two daughters of Godwin, who practise his theories; one LB's.' On May the 29th he gives a racy if rather inaccurate account of Shelley's life up to this point: 'Gone through much misery, thinking he was dying; married a girl for the mere sake of letting her have the jointure that would accrue to her; recovered; found he could not agree; separated; paid Godwin's debts, and seduced his daughter; then wondered that he would not see him. The sister left the father to go with the other. Got a child. All clever and no meretricious appearance. He is very clever; the more I read his *Queen Mab*, the more beauties I find. Published at 14 a novel; got thirty pounds for it; by his second work a hundred pounds. *Mab* not published.' Neither Byron nor the Shelleys seemed to have found Polidori an especially appealing character. Both Shelley and Mary Shelley described him as

'poor Polidori', and Claire Clairmont, more strongly, wrote of 'that vile & nauseous animal Polidori'. When Polidori was dismissed by Lord Byron at the end of 1816 he returned to London, giving up medicine for the law. In 1821 he committed suicide by taking a dose of prussic acid 'that would', commented Lord Byron, 'have killed fifty Miltiades'.

74

John William Polidori
Ximenes, The Wreath
London: Longman, Hurst, Rees, Orme & Brown, 1819
THE WORDSWORTH TRUST

Polidori's father, Gaetano, was to publish some of his own verse dramas, written in Italian, in 1845, but *Ximenes* is apparently the sole surviving example of Polidori's own attempts at verse drama. Evidently Shelley and Byron had both given little encouragement to Polidori in this field; 'Shelley etc. came in the evening' Polidori writes in his diary for 15 June, 'talked of my play etc., which all agreed was worth nothing.' In a letter to Lord Byron of 17 January 1817 (entry no. 75) Polidori writes rather nervously: 'I have also a play the Duke of Athens but I fear at this you will be more inclined to laugh than anything else but as I wish to go to the Brazil and I do not think my father will help me might I ask your Lordship to read & judge it.'

75

John William Polidori
Letter to Lord Byron
Pisa, 17 January 1817
JOHN MURRAY COLLECTION

Polidori's relations with Byron were often strained, and his tone in this letter is apologetic and self-deprecatory. In a rare and, to Byron at least, uncalled-for moment of self-confidence, Polidori had once asked his employer: 'pray, what is there excepting writing poetry that I cannot do better than you'. 'First', replied Byron, 'I can hit with a pistol the keyhole of that door - Secondly, I can swim across that river to yonder point - and thirdly, I can give you a d - d good thrashing'.

My lord -
It is but a few days since I had the pleasure of writing to you and I should not so soon have troubled you with another letter but as I set off in 3 or 4 weeks at most for England by Mount Cenis & Paris I should be happy to execute any commission that you might honour me with if your Lordship directs to me at Florence either any letters or other packages you would wish to be conveyed to London you may rely upon its safe delivery immediately upon my arrival.

I wrote to Mr Hentsch about the letter your Lordship informed me was there but have had no answer. I do not know whether I shall pass thro Geneva or strike off at Chamberey but at any case when on the Genevan territory I will send him a note desiring him to direct it to you when I hope you will open it -

I have arranged the observations I have made upon

different subjects in Italy but especially medicines & surgery in the shape of a journal and I think I have got some interesting information upon the state of these two last sciences and I have at least in my own eyes put it upon paper in if not an accurate at least a clear style - might I ask your Lordship to recommend it to Murray. I have also a play the Duke of Athens but I fear at this you will be more inclined to laugh than any thing else but as I wish to go to the Brazil and I do not think my father will help me might I ask your Lordship to read & judge it. That the information in my journal (medical) is accurate I can assure you from having read it to Vacca who has corrected it when any thing was mistated. I feel very anxious about this Brazil plan and if I did not fear troubling you I should wish to ask you that if you could you would give me some means of getting recommended to some one of the English who have influence at the Portuguese court. For it would be too late after having gone there & not succeeding to come back & try to settle in any other place - I fear I ask too much of your kindness as in return I can only assure you that I am affectionately
your obliged & humble
servant
John Polidori

- Would you remember me to Mr Hobhouse - would you also tell me if Mr Shelly is in London.

76
John William Polidori
Letter to John Murray
18 June 1816
JOHN MURRAY COLLECTION

Polidori requests a copy of Coleridge's 1816 Poems, containing 'Kubla Khan' and 'Christabel'. He also praises C.R. Maturin's *Bertram*, a play Byron had recommended for performance at Drury Lane. Coleridge's attack on that play in *Biographia Literaria* seemed to Byron a personal insult, and destroyed his sympathetic concern for Coleridge himself.

Dear Sir,
We are at Campagne Diodati near Geneva. Has a Mr Gordon remitted into your hands the spoils of Waterloo. Lord Byron has ready to pass you by the first safe hand a third canto of Childe Harold. We should be much obliged to you if you would send us
Kubla Khan and Christabel & other poems of Coleridge Esqr.
Holcrofts Memoirs
Bertram of Mathurin
The Antiquary by Guy Mannering
Taylor's Translation of Pausanias
Common red tooth powder from Waith the dentist
& if you would send to 38 Grt Pulteney St at my fathers to ask for 3 vols of Crabbe with which if you would pack immediately together directed to
~~Mr~~ P. B. Shelley Esqr
at Messrs Longdills & Co
Grays Inn Square
in whose name it will be forwarded hither as he is our neighbour. We have heard of the success of Bertram with great pleasure & saw a commentary in the french papers upon your giving twelve times as much to Mr Mathurin that would flatter you
I remain yours truly
Polidori

77
Samuel Taylor Coleridge (1772-1834)
Letter to Lord Byron
22 October 1815
JOHN MURRAY COLLECTION

Mary Shelley noted in her journal that the volume of Coleridge's poems arrived in Geneva on 26 August, two days before the Shelleys' departure. Polidori, however, described Byron reading *Christabel* to Shelley on the 18th of June and recounted the following well-known anecdote:

LB repeated some verses of Coleridge's *Christabel*, of the witch's breast; when silence ensued, and Shelley suddenly shrieking and putting his hands to his head, ran out of the room with a candle. Threw water in his face, and gave him ether. He was looking at Mrs. [S], and suddenly thought of a woman he had heard of who had eyes instead of nipples, which, taking hold of his mind, horrified him.

It seems likely, therefore, that Byron, who had persuaded John Murray to publish the poems, already had a copy of the volume in his possession. Here, Coleridge is writing to Byron thanking him for his interest.

My Lord
The Christabel, which you have mentioned in so obliging a manner, was composed by me in the [year] 1797 - I should say, that the plan of the whole poem was formed and the first Book and half of the second were finished - and it was not till after my return from Germany in the year 1800 that I resumed it - and finished the second and a part of the third Book. - This is all that Mr W Scott can have seen. Before I went to Malta, I heard from Lady Beaumont, I know not whether more gratified or more surprized, that Mr Scott had recited the Christabel and expressed no common admiration. - What occurred after my return from Italy, and what the disgusts were (most certainly not originating in my own opinion or decision) that indisposed me to the completion of the Poem, I will not trouble your Lordship with. - It is not yet a Whole: and as it will be 5 Books, I meant to publish it by itself: or with another Poem entitled, the Wanderings of Cain - of which, however, as far as it was written, I have unfortunately lost the only Copy - and can remember no part distinctly but the first stanza: -
Encinctur'd with a twine of Leaves,
That leafy Twine his only Dress!
A lovely Boy was plucking fruits
In a moon-light Wilderness,
The Moon was bright, the Air was free,
And Fruits and Flowers together grew
On many a Shrub and many a Tree:
And all put on a gentle Hue
Hanging in the shadowy Air
Like a Picture rich and rare.
It was a Climate where, they say,
The Night is more belov'd than Day.
But who that beauteous Boy beguil'd,
That beauteous Boy to linger here?
Alone, by night, a little child,
In place so silent, and so wild
Has he no *Friend*, no loving Mother near?
Sir G. Beaumont, I remember, thought it the most impressive of my compositions & I shall probably compose it over again. A Lady is now transcribing the Christabel, in the form and as far as it existed before my voyage to the Mediterranean I hope to inclose it for

Cat. 78

your Lordship's gracious acceptance tomorrow or next day. I have not learnt with what motive Wordsworth omitted the original a[d]vertisement prefixed to his White Doe, that the peculiar metre and mode of narration he had imitated from the Christabel. For this is indeed the same metre, as far as the *Law* extends the metre of the Christabel not being irregular, as Southey's Thalaba or Kehama, or Scott's Poems, but uniformly measured by four Beats in each Line. In other words, I count by Beats or accents instead of syllables in the belief that a metre might be thus produced sufficiently uniform & far more malleable to the Passion & Meaning.

Shelley's nightmare image was also a Republican emblem. Illustrated below is a cup and saucer, now at the Bowes Museum, Barnard Castle, dating from 1793, the work of the French artist Blin. The cup has an allegorical bust of the goddess *Reason*, shown with two of the emblems generally attributed to her, a lion's pelt and, on her breast, an eye in a sunburst.

The Goddess Reason

78*

William Pars (engraved by William Woollett)
The Lower Part of the Valleys and Glaciers of Chamouny in Savoy
Published 4 January 1773
Engraving 33 x 48.5 cms
THE ALPINE CLUB

Shelley visited Chamonix from Geneva in July, and the encounter continued the process of religious enquiry he had begun with *The Necessity of Atheism*. He wrote to Peacock on 22 July 1816: 'Pinnacles of snow, intolerably bright, part of the chain connected with Mont Blanc shone thro the clouds at intervals on high. I never knew I never imagined what mountains were before. The immensity of these aerial summits excited, when they suddenly burst upon the sight, a sentiment of extatic wonder, not unallied to madness - And remember this was all one scene.'

William Pars was one of the first British artists to record the Alps in his journey of 1770 with Lord Pamlerston. His four Alpine views shown at the Royal Academy in 1771 are the first pictures of purely Alpine scenery that are known to have been exhibited in England.

79*

William Pars (Engraved by William Woollett)
The Great Frozen Valley near Chamouny in Savoy
Published 5 February 1783
Engraving 33 x 48.5 cms
THE WORDSWORTH TRUST

Cat. 79

The Shelleys visited the Mer de Glace, the 'sea of ice' on 24 July. The name Mer de Glace was probably coined by William Windham, whose account of a trip to the Alps, published in English in 1744, helped popularise the area. Shelley described the scene to Peacock:

> We have returned from visiting this glacier, the scene in truth of dizzying wonder. . . . On all sides precipitous mountains the abodes of unrelenting frost surround this vale. Their sides are banked up with ice & snow broken & heaped up & exhibiting terrific chasms. The summits are sharp & naked pinnacles whose overhanging steepness will not even permit snow to rest there. They pierce the clouds like things not belonging to this earth. The vale itself is filled with a mass of undulating ice, & has an ascent sufficiently gradual even to the remotest abysses of these horrible deserts. . . . In these regions every thing changes & is in motion. This vast mass of ice has one general progress which ceases neither day nor night. It breaks & rises forever; its undulations sink whilst others rise.'

Cat. 80

80*
Edward Ellerker Williams (1793-1822)
Mont Blanc
1819
Watercolour 10 x 16 cms
THE BRITISH LIBRARY BOARD

Edward Williams, an intimate friend of Shelley's at Pisa, was an officer in the East India Company, and spent several years in India, where Shelley's cousin Thomas Medwin was a fellow officer. In 1820 he

settled with his wife Jane in Geneva, where he renewed his acquaintance with Medwin and met another future member of the Shelley circle, Edward John Trelawny. A talented draughtsman, Williams spent much of his spare time in India making drawings of the scenery.

81*
Colour chart produced on the first ascent of Mont Blanc
8 August 8 1786
Pen and watercolour 22.5 x 33.5 cms
THE ALPINE CLUB

In 1786 a local doctor, Michel Paccard, and his guide Jacques Balmat, achieved the first ascent of Mont Blanc. Dr. Paccard prepared this colour chart before the ascent, hoping to establish the exact colour of the sky at the summit. The result of his test is not recorded.

Cat. 82

82*
Percy Bysshe Shelley
Mont Blanc
1816
BARCLAYS BANK PLC

'What were virtue, love, patriotism, friendship', Shelley asks in his *Defence of Poetry* (1820), 'what were the scenery of this beautiful universe which we inhabit; what were our consolations on this side of the grave and what were our aspirations beyond it, if poetry did not ascend to bring light and fire from those eternal regions where the owl-winged faculty of calculation dare not ever soar.' *Mont Blanc*, he writes in the *History of a Six Weeks' Tour*, 'was composed under the immediate impression of the deep and powerful feelings excited by the objects which it attempts to describe; and, as an undisciplined overflowing of the soul, rests its claim to approbation on an attempt to imitate the untamable wildness and inaccessible solemnity from which those feelings sprang.' Thus the poem is at once a contemplation of the inaccessible majesty of Mont Blanc, 'piercing the infinite sky', and an affirmation of the strength of the poetic mind. The poem concludes:

> Mont Blanc yet gleams on high: - the power is there,
> The still and solemn power of many sights,
> And many sounds, and much of life and death.
> In the calm darkness of the moonless nights,
> In the lone glare of day, the snows descend
> Upon that Mountain; none beholds them there,
> Nor when the flakes burn in the sinking sun,
> Or the star-beams dart through them: - Winds contend
> Silently there, and heap the snow with breath
> Rapid and strong, but silently! Its home
> The voiceless lightning in these solitudes
> Keeps innocently, and like vapour broods
> Over the snow. The secret strength of things
> Which governs thought, and to the infinite dome
> Of heaven is as a law, inhabits thee!
> And what were thou, and earth, and stars, and sea,
> If to the human mind's imaginings
> Silence and solitude were vacancy?

83*
Mary Shelley
Frankenstein: or The Modern Prometheus
London: Lacking, Hughes, Harding, Mayor &
Jones, 1818
THE BRITISH LIBRARY BOARD

As befits a Gothic novel, which explores the approaches to the unconscious, *Frankenstein* was inspired by a reverie:

> I saw - with shut eyes but acute mental vision - I saw the pale student of unhallowed arts kneeling beside the thing he had put together. I saw the hideous phantasm of a man stretched out, and then, on the working of some powerful engine, show signs of life, and stir with an uneasy, half-vital motion. Frightful must it be; for supremely frightful, would be the effect of any human endeavour to mock the stupendous mechanism of the Creator of the world. His success would terrify the artist; he would rush away from his odious handwork, horror-stricken. He would hope that, left to itself, the slight spark of life which he had communicated would fade . . .

At the heart of this image is the effrontery of the modern scientist thinking he can, like the divine or nature itself, create. There is also here a feminist nuance: Mary Shelley's fictional creator is a man who is appropriating the woman's task of bringing new life into the world. Finally, there is Mary's own trauma about the female role itself; her own birth had led to the death of her mother, Mary Wollstonecraft, and in 1815 she had lost her first child.

FRANKENSTEIN;

OR,

THE MODERN PROMETHEUS.

IN THREE VOLUMES.

Did I request thee, Maker, from my clay
To mould me man ?   Did I solicit thee
From darkness to promote me ?——
           PARADISE LOST.

VOL. I.

London :
PRINTED FOR
LACKINGTON, HUGHES, HARDING, MAYOR, & JONES,
FINSBURY SQUARE.

1818.

The conversations at the Villa Diodati on 17 June 1816 were the immediate cause of Mary's 'acute mental vision'. As she wrote further, her visit with Shelley to spectacular alpine scenery entered into her imagination. Mary's powerful depiction of the meeting between Dr Frankenstein and the Creature makes use of the astonishing Mer de Glace, visited by the Shelleys on 24 July:

> I sat upon the rock that overlooks the sea of ice. A mist covered both that and the surrounding mountains. Presently a breeze dissipated the cloud, and I descended upon the glacier. The surface is very uneven, rising like the waves of a troubled sea, descending low, and interspersed by rifts that sink deep. The field of ice is almost a league in width, but I spent nearly two hours in crossing it. The opposite mountain is a bare perpendicular rock. From the side where I now stood Montanvert was exactly opposite, at the distance of a league; and above it rose Mont Blanc, in awful majesty. I remained in a recess of the rock, gazing on this wonderful and stupendous scene. The sea, or rather the vast river of ice, wound among its dependent mountains, whose aerial summits hung over its recesses. Their icy and glittering peaks shone in the sunlight over the clouds. My heart, which was before sorrowful, now swelled with something like joy; I exclaimed - 'Wandering spirits, if indeed ye wander, and do not rest in your narrow beds, allow me this faint happiness, or take me, as your companion, away from the joys of life.'
>
> As I said this I suddenly beheld the figure of a man, at some distance, advancing towards me with superhu-

man speed. He bounded over the crevices in the ice, among which I had walked with caution; his stature, also, as he approached, seemed to exceed that of man.

84*
John William Polidori
Ernestus Berchtold; or, The Modern Oedipus
London: Longman, Hurst, Rees, Orme & Brown, 1819
THE WORDSWORTH TRUST [THE BRITISH LIBRARY BOARD]

In his introduction to this work, Polidori gives an account of the competition held at the Villa Diodati:

> The tale here presented to the public is the one I began at Coligny, when Frankenstein was planned, and when a noble author having determined to descend from his lofty range, gave up a few hours to a tale of terror, and wrote the fragment published at the end of the Mazeppa. Though I cannot boast of the horrible imagination of the one, or the elegant classical style of the latter, still I hope the reader will not throw mine away, because it is not equal to these.

The noble author is of course Lord Byron, whose contribution to the competition was a story concerning a vampire. In her preface to *Frankenstein*, Mary Shelley wrote that 'Poor Polidori had some terrible idea about a skull-headed lady who was so punished for peeping through a keyhole - what to see I forget - something very shocking and wrong of course'. *Ernestus Berchtold*, however, makes no mention of such a lady.

85*
John William Polidori (1795-1821)
The Vampyre; A Tale
London: Sherwood, Neely & Jones, 1819
THE WORDSWORTH TRUST [THE BRITISH LIBRARY BOARD]

The Vampyre was published anonymously by Polidori in 1819, and was believed to be by Byron. It achieved much popularity both in England and on the Continent. In 1819 in Vienna, for example, Ludwig van Beethoven, searching for a subject for a new opera, is known to have bought a copy of *Der Vampyr* and Byron's *The Corsair*. *The Vampyre* was later made into an opera by Marschner and Lindpaintner in 1828. Byron began and abandoned his story on the theme of a vampire in June 1816. Polidori clearly developed the idea and published the tale in 1819.

86*
Du Vampire ou Les Grottes de Staffa
13 July 1820
Playbill
THE WORDSWORTH TRUST

The French playbill states that the play has drawn upon a work by Lord Byron. The play proved very popular in France, and a part of Dumas's *Memoires* is occupied by an account of its production.

Cat. 87

87
Matthew Gregory Lewis (1775-1818)
Portrait by Henry William Pickersgill
1809
Oil on Canvas 74.3 x 61.6 cms
NATIONAL PORTRAIT GALLERY, LONDON

M.G. 'Monk' Lewis arrived at Diodati on 14 August 1816. 'See Apollo's Sexton,' writes Shelley in Mary Shelley's journal on 18 August, 'who tells us many mysteries of his trade'. The genial author of *The Monk*, however, now aged 41 and having only two more years to live, was now more interested in his Jamaican plantations than in the supernatural. Although an incompetent rider, Lewis was a tireless conversationalist, and the flow of talk continued even while he was falling off his horse.

88
Matthew Gregory 'Monk' Lewis (1775-1818)
Ambrosio or The Monk: A Romance
London: J.Bell, 1798
THE WORDSWORTH TRUST

'What do you think of my having written, in the space of ten weeks, a romance of between three and four hundred pages octavo?' wrote Lewis to his mother in the autumn of 1794, 'I have even written out half of it fair. It is called 'The Monk', and I am so pleased with it, that if the Booksellers will not buy it, I shall publish it myself. *The Monk* was published in 1795, and made its twenty year-old author immediately famous. Shelley's gothic novels, *Zastrozzi* and *St. Irvyne* imitate its lurid gothic style.

Claire Clairmont

'Every thing is so awkward', Claire Clairmont wrote to Byron at Geneva in 1816. A year earlier she had, briefly, been Byron's mistress in London, and by 1816 she was carrying his child. Her motives in travelling to Switzerland were not only to introduce Byron to Shelley, but to confront him over their own, difficult situation.

Claire's subsequent relations with Byron were marked by her frustration at his continuing indifference towards her, and by violent disagreements concerning the upbringing of their child, Allegra. In 1821 Byron had placed Allegra in a convent in Italy, much against Claire's wishes, and the child died there of typhoid in the following year, aged five. In her fury and grief, Claire blamed Byron for her death.

Claire never married, working after Shelley's death as a governess in such diverse cities as Florence, Vienna and Moscow, all the time showing the strength of character and intellectual independence that had prompted Shelley, in *Epipsychidion*, to describe her as a 'Comet, beautiful and fierce / Who drew the heart of this frail Universe / Towards thine own.'

In the spring of 1878, shortly before her eightieth birthday, Claire was questioned about Byron, and replied:

'In 1815, when I was a very young girl, Byron was the rage . . . I was young, and vain, and poor. He was so famous that people, and especially young people, hardly considered him as a man at all, but rather as a god. The result you know. I am too old now to play with any mock repentance.'

89*
Claire Clairmont (1798-1879)
Portrait by Amelia Curran
1819
Oil on canvas 42.5 x 35.5 cms
NEWSTEAD ABBEY

At Rome in 1819 Amelia Curran painted portraits of
Shelley, Mary Shelley, their son William, and Claire
Clairmont. 'What has become of our pictures?' Mary
Shelley wrote to Curran on 20 June 1820, adding,
'Claire is not yet reconciled to hers.' Edward
Trelawny, however, who owned this portrait of
Claire, thought it a good likeness, and wrote to her
in 1823:

> 'Dearest, I have got possession of a portrait of you - by
> Miss Curran - it is an excellent likeness - free from the
> common fault of flattering, I suppose from being taken
> by a woman; its possession has given me more delight
> than I have felt since our separation, - and henceforth it
> shall be my inseparable companion - it is always before
> me.'

90*
Claire Clairmont
Diary
15 August - Mid-November 1814
THE BRITISH LIBRARY BOARD

Claire's entry for Friday October 7 shows that she
was peculiarly susceptible to supernatural 'visitations', a trait that Shelley was evidently keen to
exploit:

> at one the conversation turned upon those unaccount-
> able & mysterious feelings about supernatural things
> that we are sometimes subject to - Shelley looks beyond
> all passing strange - a look of impressive deep & melan-
> choly awe - I cannot describe it I well know how I felt
> it - I ran upstairs to bed - I placed the candle on the
> drawers & stood looking at a pillow that lay in the very
> middle of the Bed - I turned my head round to the
> window & then back again to the Bed - the pillow was no
> longer there - it had been removed to the chair - I stood
> thinking for two moments - how did this come? Was it
> possible that I had deluded myself so far as to place it
> there myself & then forget the action? This was not
> likely - *Every passed at it where in a moment - I ran
> down stairs - Shelley heard me & came out of his room
> - he gives the most horrible description of my counte-
> nance - I did not feel in the way he thinks I did - We sat
> up all night - I was ill - At day break we examined the
> room & found everything in the state I described -

*Editors have misunderstood the meaning of Claire's
careless handwriting, which clearly should have read:
'Everything passed, as it were, in a moment'.

91*
Claire Clairmont
Diary
1 January - 20 April 1818
THE BRITISH LIBRARY BOARD

Shelley and Mary report a 'curious adventure' at
Como in North Italy. When travelling to Como
Shelley carried a loaded pistol. On arrival he sought
a private place to fire it, and so render it safe. Two
policeman noticed him and feared that he meant to
commit suicide. Mary had to vouch for his good
intentions.

92*
Claire Clairmont
Diary
7 March - 1 August 1820
THE BRITISH LIBRARY BOARD

Claire's brief entry for 7 June 1819 in Rome, 'at
noon-day', announces the death of the Shelleys'
eldest son, William.

93*
Claire Clairmont
Diary
5 August 1820 - 20 September 1822
THE BRITISH LIBRARY BOARD

Claire's ironic spirit shows itself as she invents subjects for cartoons relating to Byron and Shelley.

> Caricature for poor S. He looking very sweet & smiling.
> A little Jesus Christ playing about the room He says.
> Then grasping a small knife & looking mild I'll quietly
> murder that little child. Another. Himself & God
> Almighty. He says If you please God Almighty, I'd
> rather be dammed with Plato & Lord Bacon than go to
> Heaven with Paley & Malthus. God Almighty. It shall
> be quite as you please, pray don't stand upon ceremony.
> Shelley's three aversions. God Almighty, Lord Chan-
> cellor & didactic Poetry.

Claire's primary allusion here is to Shelley's dislike
of Christianity for its cruel iconography of the
crucifixion. Panthea, in *Prometheus Unbound*, speaks
of:

> A woeful sight - a youth
> With patient looks nailed to a crucifix

94*
Lord Byron (1788-1824)
Portrait by G.H. Harlow
*c.*1815
Pencil and watercolour H 22.5 cms
PRIVATE COLLECTION

This is the original drawing of one the most popular
images of Byron, which was circulated through the
engraving by H. Meyer, and first published on 8
August 1815 by Henry Colburn in the *New Monthly
Magazine*. It was the image Shelley himself requested
from his publisher, Charles Ollier on 14 March 1817:

> Mr. Hunt has, I believe, commissioned you to get me a
> *proof* impression of a print done from a drawing by
> Harlowe of Lord Byron: I said it should be framed in

oak, but I have changed my mind and wish it to be finished in black.

95
Lord Byron
Portrait by George Brown
1826
Pencil 9.5 x 8 cms
DEREK WISE COLLECTION

This one of the drawings probably derived from Meyer's prints. Leigh Hunt records that his wife told Shelley that Byron appeared as 'a great schoolboy who had a plain bun given to him instead of a plum one.'

96*
Claire Clairmont
Letter to Lord Byron
London, 1816
JOHN MURRAY COLLECTION

Claire Clairmont, aged seventeen, makes an assignation with Lord Byron in April 1816. One of the results was her pregnancy and the subsequent birth of Allegra.

> Lord Byron is requested to state whether seven o-clock this evening will be convenient to him to receive a lady to communicate with him on business of peculiar importance. She desires to be admitted alone & with the utmost privacy. If the hour she has mentioned is correct at that hour she will come; if not will his Lordship have the goodness to make his own appointment which shall be hastily attended to though it is hoped the interview may not be postponed after this evening. - Sunday morning.

97*
Claire Clairmont
Letter to Lord Byron
Geneva, 1816
JOHN MURRAY COLLECTION

'Everything is so awkward'. So Claire found matters when she reached Geneva and found she could not be open about her liaison with Byron. Whether Shelley really was in ignorance about the state of her relations with Byron, as her suggestion that he would not see the letter hints, is not really clear.

> I would have come to you to-night if I thought I could be of *any use* to you. If you *want* me or any thing of, or belonging to me I am sure Shelley would come and fetch me if you ask him. I am afraid to come dearest for fear of meeting any one. Can you pretext the copying. Tell me any time I shall come & I will because you will have then made your arrangements. Every thing is so awkward. We go so soon. Dearest pray come and see us pray do. Good bye. I cannot find a wafer S. says he won't look at my note so don't be offended. Good bye dearest. Pray come & see us.

98*
Claire Clairmont
Letter to Lord Byron
Bath, 12 September 1816
JOHN MURRAY COLLECTION

Although Claire tells Byron 'I am melancholy and ill-humoured & low spirited' she courageously tries to write in a lively and intimate tone.

> We are arrived here and are settled. Shelley is in London but will soon come down. We had a letter from him to-day wherein he mentions having called upon Murray with your "Childe" -- he does not say whether Murray thought it long or short or what but adds he complimented him on *his* Poem & said every body praised it which shews what a mean spirited paltry soul he is & fit for nothing in the world but to give you *heaps* of money. I know I would not spare him.
>   . . . I am sure you will be very sorry to hear poor Shelley has dreadful health violent spasms in the head; this is all that vile & nauseous animal Polidori's doing -- he will do you some mischief so pray send him away & hire a steady clever physician; with your health you must not be without one. I don't know what is the matter with me but I am in no humour to write & poor *Albe* will have the dullest letter in the World. Shelley mentions likewise Murray presenting him with a copy of your Poems bound in blue & gold. Your *favourite* Mary is *impertinent* and *nauseous* enough to think it wonderful you should have remembered your promises. Bath is a very fine airy town, built up the sides of hills in high terraces but it seems very dull to me as does everything. I hope your news from England has been good & that all the people you love are as happy and well as you wish them. My dearest Albe you said you would write will you keep that promise. You can't conceive how happy it would make me only just to see your handwriting. Tell me all you have seen & how your health is. I wonder whether you *ever* think the least of me. I dare say not. I am melancholy and ill-humoured & low spirited & so I won't write any more. I have read through the first volume of the Antiquary & think it stupid. Glenarvon we are going to read. Take care of your health the greatest care & love me a little who love you so much.
> Ever quite affectionately
> Clara
>
> P.S. Mary makes me open my letter to put in remembrances & good wishes & likings. A "itty babe" would I am sure crow to see you. I am sure I should die of Joy. Please to direct to me under cover to Shelley Longdill's Gray's Inn Square. Write to me pray dearest. pray do.

99
Claire Clairmont
Letter to Lord Byron
Great Marlow, 12 January 1818
JOHN MURRAY COLLECTION

In this letter Claire romantically imagines Byron's future affection for their child after she has given her up to his care. After defending herself against impudent declarations - 'I want dignity. I do not like our Mary sail my steady course like a ship under a gentle

& favourable wind. But at thirty I shall be better' - she reports on the publication of *Frankenstein*: '. . . a most wonderful performance full of genius . . . whatever private feelings of envy I may have at not being able to do so well myself yet all yields when I consider she is a woman & will prove in time an ornament to us & an argument in your favour.'

My Dearest Friend

 This is my little darling's first Birthday so I think I cannot do better than to write you a letter. . . . My dear friend how I envy you. You will have a little darling to crawl to your knees & pull you till you take her up - then she will sit in the crook of your arm & you will give her raisins out of your own plate & a little drop of wine from your own glass & she will think herself a little Queen in Creation. When she shall be older she will run about your house like a lapwing; if you are miserable her light careless voice will make you happy. But there is one delight above all this: if it shall please you, you may delight yourself in contemplating a creature growing under your own hands as it were. You may look at her and think "this is my work." I have observed one thing in you which I like; it is this. Let a person depend on you, let them be utterly weak & defenceless, having no Instructor but yourself and you infallibly grow fond of that person. How kind and gentle you are to Children! How good-tempered & considerate towards your servants, how accommodating even to your dogs! And all this because you are sole master & lord; because there is no disputing your power you become merciful & just: but let one more on a par with yourself into the room you begin to suspect & be cautious & are consequently very often cruel. I hope therefore that I shall at least be happy enough to see you fond of the darling. What a beautiful sight it is to see a child leaning against a parent & turning up their wondering eyes in astonishment at the extraordinary thing he is saying.

 Perhaps you have been astonished that you have not seen your little girl arrive before now. But the difficulties of such a plan are innumerable. How careless were you to every feeling when you proposed to send her in the care of a nurse. Do you think I would trust her with such a person. She is all my treasure - the little creature occupies all my thoughts, all my time & my feelings - when I hold her in my arms I think to myself - there is nothing else in the world that is of you or belongs to you - you are utterly a stranger to every one else: without this little being you would hold no relations with any single human being. You might as well have asked a miser to trust his gold for a sea voyage in a leaking vessel. Besides various and ceaseless misgivings that I entertain of you. Suppose that in yielding her to your care I yield her to neglect and coldness! How am I assured that such will not be the case? Since it is as I have before written that I have observed that generosity in your disposition towards defenceless creatures but at the same time on so important a point I feel tremors of doubt & uncertainty. I so fear she will be unhappy. I am so anxious to be cautious - to do nothing hastily - & to consider & examine all things. Poor little angel! in your great house, left perhaps to servants while you are drowning sense & feeling in wine & striving all you can to ruin the natural goodness of your nature who will there be to watch her. She is peculiarly delicate - her indigestions are frequent & dangerous if neglected - a moment might take from me all I hold dear - a moment might create for me memories long & dread too terrible even in this instant's conception. Do not think me selfish - whatever I may be to others with her I cannot

be so. My affections are few & therefore strong - the extreme solitude in which I live has concentrated them to one point and that point is my lovely child. I study her pleasure all day long - she is so fond of me that I hold her in my arms till I am nearly falling on purpose to delight her. We sleep together and if you knew the extreme happiness I feel when she nestles closer to me, in listening to our regular breathing together. I could tear my flesh in twenty thousand different directions to ensure her good and when I fear for her residing with you it is not the dread I have to commence the long series of painful anxiety I know I shall have to endure it is best I should behold her richly & wasted with improper management lest I should live to hear that *you* neglected her. My dearest friend if all this while your feelings are good & gentle then have I done you an irreparable wrong in thus suspecting you. & most sincerely am I grieved for I well remember my own silent though bitter burnings when you would often half in jest accuse me of thought & actions which I detested. I cannot pardon those who attribute to me rude & indelicate feelings; or who believe because I have unloosed myself from the trammels of custom & opinion that I do not possess within a severer monitor than either of these; who do not behold in the height & loftiness of my hopes the securing & pledge of my purity and innocence. I have loved it is true but what then? Have you suffered through me or my love? Find me the person who will say that with me. Find me another human being who has borne unkindness & injustice with the patience & gentleness I have? I have a child and shew me a better a more attentive fond mother. When affection & tenderness, when sacrifice & generosity shall be demonstrated as odious then may I be classed among selfish & detestable beings but not before.

 This long *tirade* as you will call it has been drawn from me by my hearing repeated some expressions of yours concerning me which makes you better want of discrimination in you if you really thought as you spoke which I do not believe. Though I have thus praised myself I am not vain in that: how should I be otherwise living in the company I do. Indeed I ought to be better. Alone I study Plutarch's Lives wherein I find nothing but excitements to virtue & abstinence: with Mary & Shelley the scene changes but from the contemplation of the virtues of the dead to those of the living. I have no Hobhouse by my side to dispirit me with an easy & impudent declaration of "the villainy of all mankind" which I can construe into nothing but an attempt to cover his conscious unworthiness. I must be the veriest wretch if I were wicked placed in such a situation as I am. I have faults. I am timid from vanity; my temper is inconstant & . . . I want dignity I do not like our Mary sail my steady course like a ship under a gentle & favorable wind. But at thirty I shall be better and every year I hope to gain in value.

 What news shall I tell you? Mary has just published her first work a novel called Frankenstein or, the Modern Prometheus. It is a most wonderful performance full of genius & the fiction is of so continued and extraordinary a kind as no one would imagine could have been written by so young a person. I am delighted & whatever private feelings of envy I may have at not being able to do so well myself yet all yields when I consider that she is a woman & will prove in time an ornament to us & an argument in our favour. How I delight in a lovely woman of strong & cultivated intellect. How I delight to hear all the intricacies of mind & argument hanging on her lips! If she were my mortal enemy, if she had even injured my darling I would serve her with fidelity and fervently advocate her as doing good to the whole. When I read of Epichasis the slave in Tacitus & of Hypatia of Alexandria in Gibbon, I shriek with joy & cry Vittoria! Vittoria! I cannot bear that women should be outdone in virtue & knowledge by [The last page is missing]

100
Claire Clairmont
Letter to Lord Byron
24 March 1821
The British Library Board

Claire passionately opposes Byron's plan to place Allegra in a convent.

I have just received the letter which announces the putting of Allegra into a Convent - Before I quitted Geneva you promised me, verbally it is true, that my child, whatever its sex, would never be put away from one of its parents. This promise originated in my being afflicted at your idea of placing it under Mrs Leigh. This promise is violated not only slightly but in a mode and by a conduct most intolerable to my feelings as well for Allegra. It has been my desire & my practise to interfere with you as little as possible but were I silent now, you would adopt this as an argument against me at some future period. I therefore represent to you that the putting Allegra at her years away from any relative into a Convent is to me a serious & deep affliction. Since you first gave the hint of your design, I have been at some pains to enquire into their system and I find that the state of the children is nothing less than most miserable. I see no reason to believe that Convents are better regulated at Ravenna, a secondary, out of the way town of the Roman States than at Florence, the capital of Tuscany. Every traveller & every writer upon Italy joins in condemning them, which would be alone sufficient testimony, without adverting to the state of ignorance & profligacy of the Italian women, or pupils of Convents. They are bad wives & most unnatural mothers, licentious & ignorant - they are the dishonour & unhappiness of society. This then, with every advantage in your power, and wealth, friends, is the education that you have chosen for your daughter, this step will procure to you an innumerable addition of enemies and blame, for it can be regarded as in one light by the virtuous of whatever sect or denomination. Allegra's misfortune in being condemned to a life of ignorance & deprivation, in being deprived of the advantages which the belonging to the most enlightened country entitle her to and of the protection & friendship of her parents friends (so essential to the well-being of a child in her desolate situation by the adoption of a different religion and of an education, known to be contemptible, will be received by the world as a perfect fulfilment on your part of all the censures past upon you. How will Lady Byron never yet justified for her conduct towards you be soothed & rejoice in the honourable safety of herself & child and all the world be bolder to praise her prudence, my unhappy Allegra burnishing the condemning evidence. I alone, misled by love to believe you good, trusted to you & now I reap the fruits.

. . . I resigned Allegra to you that she might be benefitted by advantages which I could not give her. It was natural for me to expect that your daughter would become an object of affection and would receive an education becoming the child of an english nobleman.

Cat. 100

Since however you are indifferent to her, or that the purity of your principles does not allow you to cherish a natural child I entreat you as an act of justice to allow the following scheme to be put into execution that Allegra may have the benefits her mother can procure to her. I propose to place her at my own expense in one of the best English boarding schools where if she is deprived of the happiness of a home & paternal cares, she at least would receive an English education which would enable her after many years of painful & unprotected childhood to be benefitted by the kindness & affection of her parents' friends - This school shall be chosen by your own friends, I will see her only so often as they shall decide because I hope to induce you by this sacrifice of myself to yield the child to proper hands. By adopting this plan, you will save your child and also the expense: anxiety for her safety & well being need never trouble you, you will become as free as if you had no such ties. I entreat you earnestly not to be obstinate on this point: believe me in putting Allegra into a Convent to ease yourself of the trouble and to hurt me in my affection for her you have done almost a greater misery to yourself than either to her or me. So blind is hatred! I have already mentioned the evil to your reputation besides which in separating her from you at this early age her attachment is weakened and the difference of religion added to the evil stories concerning you will in a few years more completely alienate her from you. Such is the miserable & unsatisfactory state, produced by this step to all three. To none does it procure an atom of advantage or pleasure. Add another remark upon this Convent scheme if it is a place suited to Allegra why need you to pay a double pension to ensure her a proper treatment & attention. This little fact coming from yourself, says everything in condemnation of the plan.

I know not how to address you in terms fit to awaken acquiescence to the above requests: yet neither know why I should doubt the wisdom of propriety of what I propose, seeing that I have never with regard to Allegra sought anything but her advantage even at the price of total unhappiness to myself. "My heart" to use the words of an author "is rather wise because it loves much than because it knows much." and the great affection I feel for her makes me to arrive at the

Cat. 89 Claire Clairmont by Amelia Curran

Cat. 94 Lord Byron by G.H. Harlow

knowledge of what is her good, almost as if it were instinctively. I pray you to allow yourself to be advised in this point and I mention Mad. Hoppner because she is frindlil [sic] disposed towards you and enabled by her situation to judge fairly what difference exists between an Italian & english education.

You would have had this letter much sooner but that I was absent at Florence when the letter from Ravenna arrived at Pisa. They, not willing to annoy me when on a visit kept it some time but as my stay became longer, sent it to me. I beg you will address to Pisa as usual, to which city I return in another week. I cannot say how anxiously I expect your answer: since I read the letter I have not had a moment's content fearing to allow myself the ease, lest Allegra should be suffering from neglect, nor can I be happy until some plan is decided upon of a real advantage to her. I am desirous also of knowing how far Bayna Cavallo is from Ravenna and if on the sea coast. Also whether Allegra is entered for a short time or for a fixed period. The answer to these questions is of the greatest importance to me. Again I entreat you to yield so that we may both be easy about her: I, not suffering from anxiety & injury, nor you from the contention in your breast of hatred & pride which my entreaties awaken. I know that expressions of affection & friendship only exasperate you yet I cannot help wishing you as much happiness as you inflict an unjust misery upon me. Then indeed you would be blessed.
Claire

101*
Claire Clairmont
Letter to Lord Byron
Florence, 18 February 1822
THE BRITISH LIBRARY BOARD

Claire requests a meeting with her daughter in reasonable terms, but Byron's consistent failure to answer her letters eventually drove her to propose snatching Allegra from the convent. 'No exertions of yours can obtain Allegra,' advised Shelley in reponse, 'and believe me that the plans you have lately dreamed, would, were they attempted only, plunge you and all that is connected with you in ruin irredeemable'.

I am extremely glad to hear that by your succession to a large fortune, your affairs have become more prosperous than ever. I wish and pray that you may have health to enjoy yourself many more years with every other accordant circumstance that can combine to make a person happy. You will perhaps not believe that I sincerely wish this for your sake's and therefore I shall venture to wish it for Allegra's - I do not say that I write now upon her account, but on the contrary solely upon my own. I assure you I can no longer resist the internal inexplicable feeling which haunts me that I shall never see her any more. I entreat you to destroy this feeling by allowing me to see her. I waited two months in the Autumn, expecting from all you professed to see her every week and when on the sudden you would no longer allow it to be a melancholy tearfulness came over one which has never since passed away. This was owing to the cruel disappointment I felt and which may perhaps mislead my judgement, but to what besides a determined hatred can I attribute your conduct? I have often entreated Shelley to intercede for me and he invariably answers that it is utterly useless. I am not

wanting in feelings of Pride but every thing yields to the extent of my present unhappiness which grows daily towards Despair, and induces me to address you in hopes of an alleviation of my misery. If I could only flatter myself that you would not harden your heart against me I would indulge the hope that you would grant me what I ask.

I shall shortly leave Italy, for a new country to enter upon a disagreeable and precarious course of life; I yield in this not to my own wishes, but to the advice of a friend whose head is wiser than mine - I leave my friends with regret but indeed I cannot go without having first seen and embraced Allegra - Do not I entreat you refuse me this little but only consolation. If instead of the friendly office I request, you resolve to humiliate me by a refusal, success in what I attempt will be impossible for I know not where I shall gather even the spirit to begin it. I have experienced that I can conquer every feeling but those of Nature; these grave themselves on the breast with thorns, and while Life lasts, they make their sharpness felt. I am sensible how little this letter is calculated to persuade; but it is one of my unhappinesses that I cannot write to you with the deepness which I feel; because I know how much you are prejudiced against me and the constraint which this inspires, weakens and confuses all I would express. But if you refuse me where shall I hope for any thing?

The weather is fine, the passage of the Appenines is free and safe. The when and where of our meeting shall be entirely according to your pleasure and with every restriction and delicacy that you think necessary for Allegra's sake. I shall abandon myself to Despair if you refuse: but indeed if your reason, my dear friend cannot be persuaded to alter the line of conduct, you have hitherto pursued in all that regards Allegra, it were better that I were dead. So I should escape all the suffering which your harshness causes me. But Hope in the present state of my spirits is necessary to me and I will believe that you will kindly consent to my wish. How inexpressibly dearly will I not cherish your name and recollection, as the author of my happiness in the far off places to which I am obliged to go, and amidst the strangers who will surround me. My dear friend I conjure you do not make the world dark to me as if my Allegra were dead. In the happiness her sight will cause me I shall gain restoration and strength to enable me to bear the mortifications and displeasures to which a poor and unhappy person is exposed in the world. I wish you every happiness.
Claire

102
Lord Byron
Letter to John Murray
7 June 1819
THE BRITISH LIBRARY BOARD

Byron boasts to Murray about his daughter Allegra, now living with him: 'My daughter Allegra was well too and is growing pretty - her hair is growing darker and her eyes are blue. - her temper and her ways Mr. Hoppner says are like mine - as well as her features. - she will make in that case a manageable young lady.' He complains he hears nothing of his daughter Ada from Lady Byron: 'the moral Clytemnestra is not very communicative of her tidings - but there will come a day of reckoning.'

Cat. 105

Cat. 104

103
Lord Byron
Letter to John Murray
Venice, 22 October 1819
THE BRITISH LIBRARY BOARD

Byron plans to leave to go to Venezuela: 'I should not make a bad South-American planter, and I should take my natural daughter Allegra with me and settle.'

104*
Byron and Allegra
Portrait by Richard Westall
Watercolour 8 x 6 cms
JOHN MURRAY COLLECTION

According to a pencil note on the back of the sketch this is a portrait of Byron and Allegra by R. Westall. It is possible however that it represents Byron and Mary Chaworth's daughter by H. Corbould. There is no especial likeness between Allegra here and the genuine miniature of Allegra below.

105*
Allegra, aged one and a half years
Portrait by unknown artist
Watercolour 7 x 7 cms
JOHN MURRAY COLLECTION

On the back of the frame is the following inscription: 'Portrait of Allegra Biron Daughter of George Gordon Lord Byron etc etc etc - aged one year and six months. Venice - 1818. -' On 13 January 1818 Byron wrote to Douglas Kinnaird:

> Shelley (from Marlow) has written to me about my Daughter (the last bastard one) who it seems is a great beauty . . . I shall acknowledge and breed her myself - giving her the name of *Biron* (to distinguish her from little Legitimacy) - and mean to christen her Allegra - which is a Venetian name.

106
G. Cruikshank (1792-1878)
Fare thee well
1816
Photograph after engraving
THE WORDSWORTH TRUST

Byron is shown embracing Mrs Charlotte Mardyn, the Drury Lane actress, while two further actresses clasp his legs. He is waving goodbye to Lady Byron, who watches from a cliff holding their daughter Ada. Two sailors on a neighbouring ship wonder if Byron has enough actresses to last the trip. Byron's separation was widely publicised, and the unauthorised publication of 'Fare thee well', served only to increase the poet's notoriety. The suggestion that Mrs Mardyn had anything to do with Byron's separation from his wife was a false rumour.

England: 1816-1818

Soon after his return from Switzerland in September 1816 Shelley heard the news that his wife, heavily pregnant, had taken her own life. 'Harriet's suicide had a beneficial effect on Shelley', recalled Claire Clairmont more than sixty years later, 'he became much less confident in himself and not so wild as he had been before.' And indeed Shelley's life from 1816 is much more settled. For the first time, more than a few months was spent in a particular setting. At Albion House in Marlow, Buckinghamshire, Shelley established the life of quiet reading and study that he struggled to maintain throughout his years of exile. On 23 April 1817 Shelley wrote to Byron:

> We spend our time here in that tranquil uniformity which presents much to enjoy and leaves nothing to record. I have my books, and a garden with a lawn, enclosed by high hedges, and overshawdowed by firs and cypresses intermixed with apple trees now in blossom. We have a boat on the river, in which, when the days are sunny and serene, such as we have had of late, we sail.

Shelley's political concerns remained, but his radicalism now began to express itself in more purely poetic terms. *Alastor*, which was published in February 1816, is a poem 'allegorical of one of the most interesting situations of the human mind', the first work in which Shelley questions the inevitable disappointment and solitude of idealism. *The Revolt of Islam*, published in 1818, now has the political idealism of the earlier *Queen Mab*, 'interwoven with a story of human passion'. Shelley's energetic desire for improvement was now tempered and illuminated by an awareness of human limitations and weaknesses. In his preface to the poem he cautions against the quick, unthinking optimism that turned the French Revolution into a tragedy:

> Can he who the day before was a trampled slave suddenly become liberal-minded, forebearing and independent? . . . Such is the lesson which experience teaches us now. But, on the first reverses of hope in the progress of French liberty, the sanguine eagerness for good overleaped the solution of these questions, and for a time extinguished itself in the unexpectedness of their result.'

Shelley began to develop lasting literary friendships. Thomas Love Peacock, his neighbour at Marlow, had been a friend since 1812, and was a constant visitor to Albion House. Like Shelley, he had an outstanding knowledge of the classics. Leigh Hunt, with his wife Marianne, had been kind to Shelley immediately following Harriet's suicide, and at their home at the Vale of Health, Hampstead, the poet would meet members of the Hunt circle, including William Hazlitt, Benjamin Robert Haydon and, most importantly, John Keats, who seems to have treated Shelley with a degree of caution. Hunt's son Thornton Shelley:

> I can remember with well one day when we were both for some long time engaged in gambols, broken off by my terror at his screwing up his long and curling hair into a horn and approaching me with rampant paws and frightful gestures as some imaginative monster. . . . I am well aware that he *had* suffered severely, and that he continued to be haunted by certain recollections, partly real and partly imaginative, which pursued him like an Orestes.

Hunt saw poetry as, among other things, a form of social entertainment, and, always at his best in sympathetic company, Shelley would even participate in sonnet competitions with men such as the urbane and witty Horace and James Smith. With Mary and Peacock he visited the opera, saw Mozart's *Don Giovanni*, and visited the British Museum, where he could see the great statue of Ramases II (also known as Ozymandias).

107*

Harriet Shelley (1795-1816)
Letter to Catherine Nugent
London, 20 November [1814]
THE BRITISH LIBRARY BOARD

Harriet is writing soon after her separation from Shelley to her Irish friend Catherine Nugent. In her anger and disillusionment she describes Shelley as a 'vampire', and blames the separation on the 'false doctrines' of Godwin's *Political Justice*.

My Dearest Mrs Nugent,

Your fears are verified. Mr. Shelley has become profligate and sensual, owing entirely to Godwin's 'Political Justice'. The very great evil that book has done is not to be told. The false doctrines therein contained have poisoned many a young and virtuous mind. Mr Shelley is living with Godwin's two daughters - one by Mary Wollstonecraft the other the daughter of his present wife, called Clairmont. I told you some time back Mr. Shelley was to give Godwin three thousand pounds. It was in effecting the accomplishment of this scheme that he was obliged to be at Godwin's house, and Mary was determined to secure him. She is to blame. She heated his imagination by talking of her mother, going to her grave with him every day, till at last she told him she was dying in love for him, accompanied with the most violent gestures and vehement expostulations. He thought of me and my sufferings, and begged her to get the better of a passion as degrading to him as to herself. She then told him she would die - he had rejected her, and what appeared to her as the sublimest virtue was to him a crime. Why could we not all live together? I as his sister, She as his wife? He had the folly to believe this possible, and sent for me, then residing at Bath. You may suppose how I felt at the disclosure. I was laid up for a fortnight after. I could do nothing for myself. He begged me to live. The doctors gave me over. They said 'twas impossible. I saw his despair. The agony of my beloved sister; and owing to the great strength of my constitution I lived; and here I am, my dear friend, waiting to bring another infant into this woful world. Next month I shall be confined. He will not be near me. No, he cares not for me now. He never asks after me or sends me word how he is going on. In short, the man I once loved is dead. This is a vampire. His character is blasted for ever. Nothing can save him now. Oh! If you knew what I have suffered, your heart would drop blood for my misery. When may I expect to see you? Do tell me, my dear friend, and write soon. Eliza is at Southampton with my darling babe. London does not agree with her. Will you enquire for a family of the name of Colthurst in Dublin? There is one son and daughter growing up living with the mother. I want the direction, as I know them very well.

Adieu, my dear friend, may you be happy is the best wish of her who sincerely loves you.
H. Shelley.

108*

Percy Bysshe Shelley
Letter to Mary Godwin (later Shelley)
London, 16 December 1816
THE BRITISH LIBRARY BOARD

Shelley wrote this letter to Mary Godwin upon hearing the news that his estranged wife had drowned herself in the Serpentine in the first week of December. He does not, at least consciously, accept any blame for her death; 'the beastly viper her sister', Eliza Westbrook, is the principal villain.

I have spent a day, my beloved, of somewhat agonising sensations; such as the contemplation of vice & folly & hard heartedness exceeding all conception must produce. Leigh Hunt has been with me all day & his delicate & tender attentions to me, his kind speeches of you, have sustained me against the weight of the horror of this event.

The children I have not yet got. I have seen Longdill who recommends proceeding with the utmost caution and resoluteness. He seems interested. I told him that I was under contract of marriage to you; & he said that in such an event all pretences to detain the children would cease. Hunt said very delicately that this would be soothing intelligence for you. - Yes, my only hope my darling love, this will be one among the innumerable benefits which you will have bestowed upon me, & which will still be inferior in value to that greatest of benefits - yourself - it is thro' you that I can entertain without despair the recollection of the horrors of unutterable villainy that led to this dark dreadful death.

- I am to hear tomorrow from *Desse* whether or no, I am to engage in a contest for the children. - At least it is consoling to know that if the contest should arise it would have its termination in your nominal union with me. - that after having blessed me with a life a world of real happiness, a mere form appertaining to you will not be barren of good. -

It seems that this poor woman - the most innocent of her abhorred & unnatural family - was driven from her father's house, & descended the steps of prostitution until she lived with a groom of the name of Smith, who deserting her, she killed herself - There can be no question that the beastly viper her sister, unable to gain profit from her connexion with me - has secured to herself the fortune of the old man - who is now dying - by the murder of this poor creature. Everything tends to prove, however, that beyond the mere shock of so hideous a catastrophe having fallen on a human being once so nearly connected with me, there would, in any case have been little to regret. Hookham, Longdill - every one does me full justice; bears testimony to the up{rightness &} liberality of my conduct to her: T{here} is but one voice in condemnation of the dete{s}table Westbrooks. If they should dare to bring {it} before Chancery a scene of such fearful horror would be unfolded as would cover them with scorn & shame.

How is Clare? I do not tell her, but I may tell you how deeply I am interested in her safety. I [need] not recommend her to your care. Give her any kind message from me, & calm her spirits as well as you can.

I do not ask you to calm your own I am well in health tho somewhat faint & agitated but the affectionate attentions shewn me by Hunt have been sustainers & restoratives, more than I can tell. Do you dearest & best seek happiness where it ought to reside in your own pure & perfect bosom: in the thoughts of how dear & how good you are to me how wise, & how extensively beneficial you are perhaps now destined to become. Remember my poor babes Ianthe & Charles how dear & tender a mother they will find in you Darling William too! my eyes overflow with tears. Tomorrow more. Write a long letter, & give me some answer to Hunt's messages.
P.B. Shelley

Alastor

O, for Medea's wondrous alchemy,
Which wheresoe'er it fell made the wintry earth gleam
With bright flowers, and the wintry boughs exhale
From vernal blooms fresh fragrance! O, that God,
Profuse of poisons, would concede the chalice
Which but one living man has drained, who now,
Vessel of deathless wrath, a slave that feels
No proud exemption in the blighting curse
He bears, over the world wanders for ever,
Lone as incarnate death! O, that the dream
Of dark magician in his visioned cave,
Raking the cinders of a crucible
For life and power, even when his feeble hand
Shakes in its last decay, were the true law
Of this so lovely world! But thou art fled
Like some frail exhaltation; which the dawn
Robes in its golden beams, - ah! thou hast fled!
The brave, the gentle, and the beautiful,
The child of grace and genius. Heartless things
Are done and said i' the world, and many worms
And beasts and men live on, and mighty Earth
From sea and mountain, city and wilderness,
In vesper low or joyous orison,
Lifts still its solemn voice: - but thou art fled -
Thou canst no longer know or love the shapes
Of this phantasmal scene, who have to thee
Been purest ministers, who are, alas!
Now thou art not. Upon those pallid lips
So sweet even in their silence, on those eyes
That image sleep in death, upon that form
Yet safe from the worm's outrage, let no tear
Be shed - not even in thought. Nor, when those hues
Are gone, and those divinest lineaments,
Worn by the senseless wind, shall live alone
In the frail pauses of this simple strain,
Let not high verse, mourning the memory
Of that which is no more, or painting's woe
Or sculpture, speak in feeble imagery
Their own cold powers. Art and eloquence,
And all the shows o' the world are frail and vain
To weep a loss that turns their light to shade.
It is a woe too 'deep for tears,' when all
Is reft at once, when some surpassing Spirit,
Whose light adorned the world around it, leaves
Those who remain behind, not sobs or groans,
The passionate tumult of a clinging hope;
But pale despair and cold tranquillity,
Nature's vast frame, the web of human things,
Birth and the grave, that are not as they were.

(lines 672-720)

Cat. 110

ALASTOR;

OR,

THE SPIRIT OF SOLITUDE.

AND OTHER POEMS.

BY

PERCY BYSSHE SHELLEY.

———————

LONDON:

PRINTED FOR BALDWIN, CRADOCK, AND JOY, PATER-
NOSTER ROW; AND CARPENTER AND SON,
OLD BOND-STREET:

By S. Hamilton, Weybridge, Surrey.

1816

109*
Percy Bysshe Shelley
Alastor; or, The Spirit of Solitude
London: Baldwin, Cradock, & Joy, 1816
PRIVATE COLLECTION [THE BRITISH LIBRARY BOARD]

'. . . from his return to England' writes W.B. Yeats, 'rivers and streams and wells, flowing through caves or rising in them, came into every poem of his that was of any length, and always with the precision of symbols'. *Alastor* was composed near Windsor following Shelley's excursion up the Thames with Peacock, Mary Godwin and Charles Clairmont, and the river is a constant presence in the later stages of the poem. The main character, a solitary poet, pursues 'the winding of the cavern'; he seems to move downstream, finally to reach the sea, and the ending of the individual life. Yet at the same time he is travelling upstream to another kind of life, towards the origins and never to be satisfied yearnings of the imagination. The river-journey, writes Yeats, as 'an image that has transcended particular time and place becomes a symbol, passes beyond death, as it were, and becomes a living soul'.

110
Paul Sandby (1725-1809)
Ancient Beech-Tree, Windsor Great Park
1797
Watercolour 62.5 x 44 cms
JONATHAN WORDSWORTH COLLECTION

'He spent his days under the oak-shades of Windsor Great Park', writes Mary Shelley in her note to *Alastor*, 'and the magnificent woodland is a fitting study to inspire the various descriptions of forest-scenery we find in the poem.'

> The oak,
> Expanding its immense and knotty arms,
> Embraces the light beech. The pyramids
> Of the tall cedar overarching, frame
> Most solemn domes within, and far below,
> Like clouds suspended in an emerald sky,
> The ash and the acacia floating hang
> Tremulous and pale.'

Here, Sandby suggests human littleness by placing a sleeping woodman beneath a sublime work of nature. Above, the branches snake and twist in a pale blue light. A nineteenth-century hand has added the signature of Copley Fielding, and partially erased Sandby's initials. The actual tree, which was of exceptional age, is identified by William Sandby in *Thomas and Paul Sandby* (1892).

111
Samuel Taylor Coleridge (1772-1834)
Poems
Private Printing [1812]
THE BRITISH LIBRARY BOARD

At the head of the first page of text is the inscription: 'Fanny Godwin April 14th 1814'. Fanny Godwin, usually called Fanny Imlay, was the daughter of Mary Wollstonecraft and Gilbert Imlay. On 11 October 1816 she poisoned herself at Swansea, two months before the body of Harriet Westbrook was taken from the Serpentine.

The contents of this pamphlet ('Fears in Solitude', 'France, an Ode', 'Frost at Midnight') first appeared in 1798. This edition, privately printed for Coleridge in 1812, is very rare, only some half dozen in all being recorded.

Cat. 112

112*
Albion House, Marlow
Photograph 10.5 x 18.3 cms
THE WORDSWORTH TRUST

The Shelleys moved into Albion House, Marlow in March 1817, and there Shelley sought to establish some domestic stability. Surrounded by books, Shelley would sit in the garden and read, or spend entire days in the small skiff he kept tethered on the nearby river, writing *The Revolt of Islam*. With Autumn, however, the disadvantages of Albion House's riverside location began to be felt. It grew damp, Shelley's books developed a strange kind of mould, and his health was badly affected.

Albion House is second from the left.

Cat. 113

113
Thomas Love Peacock (1785-1866)
Portrait by Henry Wallace
Dated 1858
Millboard 16.5 x 14 cms
NATIONAL PORTRAIT GALLERY, LONDON

Thomas Love Peacock, the poet and satirical novelist, was a close friend of Shelley from 1812 until the latter's death in 1822, and part of the literary group that centred around Marlowe in 1817-18. When Shelley eloped with Mary Godwin, Peacock sided sharply with Harriet, but his friendship with the poet nevertheless continued. His ironic humour refreshed Shelley and, more importantly, inspired him to re-assess and articulate his ideas. When, in 1820, Peacock published *The Four Ages of Poetry*, arguing that poetry should now give way to the superior world of reason, Shelley responded: 'Your anathemas against poetry itself excited me to a sacred rage. . . . I had the greatest possible desire to break a lance with you . . . in honour of my mistress Urania', and his greatest prose work, *A Defence of Poetry* (unpublished until 1840), soon followed.

The portrait shows Peacock in later life, after he had all but abandoned literature for a successful career at India House. In 1850 William Thackeray described him as 'a whiteheaded, jolly old worldling, and Secretary to the E. India House, full of information about India and everything else in the world.' His *Memoirs of Shelley* appeared as articles between 1858 and 1862.

114
Thomas Love Peacock
Palmyra, And Other Poems
London: T. Bensley, 1806
THE WORDSWORTH TRUST

Peacock's first literary productions, *Palmyra and Other Poems* (1806) and *The Genius of the Thames* (1810) were sent to Shelley by Thomas Hookham in August 1812, while Shelley was at Lynmouth and before the two writers had met. He was enthusiastic: 'The poems abound with a genius, an information, the power & extent of which I admire, in proportion as I lament the object of their application', he commented. 'At the same time I am free to say that [*The Genius of the Thames*] appears to be far beyond mediocrity in genius & versification, & the conclusion of 'Palmyra' the finest piece of poetry I ever read.'

115
Thomas Love Peacock
Rhododaphne: or The Thessalian Spell. A Poem
London: Baldwin, Cradock, & Joy, 1818
THE WORDSWORTH TRUST

Shelley wrote a review of this poem in 1818, which remained unpublished until 1879:

> *Rhododaphne* is a poem of the most remarkable character, and the nature of the subject no less than the spirit in which it is written forbid us to range it under any of the classes of modern literature. It is a Greek and Pagan poem. In sentiment and scenery it is essentially antique.

Shelley's own *Revolt of Islam*, published in the same year, is itself set in Greece, and has a conscious Mediterranean and pagan flavour.

116*
Thomas Love Peacock
Nightmare Abbey
London: T. Hookham Jun., 1818
THE BRITISH LIBRARY BOARD

Nightmare Abbey, Peacock's satirical novel on gothic excess, alludes to Byron, Coleridge, and, in the character of Scythrop Glowry, to Shelley himself:

> [Scythrop] now became troubled with the *passion for reforming the world. . . .* He passed whole mornings in gloomy reverie, stalking about the room in his nightcap, which he pulled over his eyes like a cowl, and folding his striped calico dreesing-gown about him like the mantle of a conspirator.

Reading the novel in Italy, Shelley wrote to Peacock: 'I am delighted with Nightmare Abbey. I

Cat. 122 Horace and James Smith by G.H. Harlow

Cat. 132 Samuel Prout, *The Rialto, Venice*

Cat. 134 G. Lanza, *Paestum*

think Scythrop a character admirably conceived & executed... I suppose the moral is contained in what Falstaff says "*For God's sake talk like a man of this world*", and yet looking deeper into it, is not the misdirected enthusiasm of Scythrop what J[esus] C[hrist] calls the salt of the earth?'

117
Thomas Love Peacock
The Misfortunes of Elphin
London: Thomas Hookham, 1829
THE WORDSWORTH TRUST

The Misfortunes of Elphin is a parody of the Arthurian legends, set in Wales. As preparation, Peacock read widely in Welsh legend.

Cat. 118

118*
James Henry Leigh Hunt (1784-1859)
Portrait by Thomas Charles Wageman
1815
Pencil 21 x 16.5 cms
NATIONAL PORTRAIT GALLERY, LONDON

Leigh Hunt, editor of the radical weekly, *The Examiner*, had been imprisoned early in 1813 for a libel on the Prince Regent. Shelley wrote to Hunt in 1816 on Byron's recommendation, sending him a copy of 'Hymn to Intellectual Beauty'. Always encouraging to young writers, Hunt promised to print the poem, and on 1 December 1816 announced in the *Examiner* the arrival of three 'Young Poets' (namely Shelley, Keats and John Hamilton Reynolds):

The object of the present article is merely to notice three young writers, who appear to us to promise a considerable addition of strength to the new school. Of the first who came before us, we have, it is true, yet seen only one or two specimens, and these were no sooner sent to us than we unfortunately mislaid them; but we shall procure what he has published, and if the rest answer to what we have seen, we shall have no hesitation in announcing him for a very striking and original thinker. His name is PERCY BYSSHE SHELLEY, and he is the author of a poetical work entitled *Alastor, or the Spirit of Solitude*.

In the event, Leigh Hunt's strong political stance meant that his literary support attracted the scorn of reviewers from the opposite political camp. *Blackwood's Magazine*, for example, labelled the new poetry 'the cockney school'. Over the years, however, Hunt's friendship was a much-valued support to the poet. *The Cenci* is dedicated to him.

119
James Henry Leigh Hunt
Portrait by Benjamin Robert Haydon
*c.*1811
Oil on canvas 61 x 50.2 cms
NATIONAL PORTRAIT GALLERY, LONDON

Benjamin Robert Haydon was a painter of portraits and historical subjects. He was a friend of Keats, Hazlitt and Leigh Hunt, and until 1820 of Wordsworth. He would sometimes meet Shelley at Hunt's home, and recalled one particular meeting in his *Autobiography* (1846):

I went a little after the time, and seated myself in the place kept for me at table right opposite Shelley himself, as I was told after, for I did not know what hectic, spare, weakly, yet intellectual-looking creature it was carving a bit of brocoli or cabbage on his plate, as if it had been the substantial wing of a chicken. Hunt and his wife and her sister, Keats, Horace Smith and myself made up the party. In a few minutes Shelley opened the conversation by saying in a most feminine and gentle voice, 'As to that detestable religion, the Christian . . .' I looked astounded, but casting a glance round the table, easily saw by Hunt's expression of ecstacy and the women's simper, I was to be set at that evening *vi et armis*.

Haydon rose to the challenge, and, later in the evening, Shellley remarked to Hunt, 'Haydon's fierce'.

120
Horatio Smith (1779-1849)
Portrait by unknown artist
Watercolour 19.1 x 16.5 cms
NATIONAL PORTRAIT GALLERY, LONDON

Horace Smith, a banker and popular writer of light verse, first met Shelley in 1816. He later remembered the poet as 'a fair, freckled, blue-eyed, light-haired, delicate-looking person, his countenance was serious and thoughtful'. Their friendship continued during Shelley's subsequent years of exile, and Smith was on his way to see Shelley when he heard of his death.

Shelley and Smith would often go to the British Museum, and a visit to the newly-acquired statue of Ramases II in 1817 prompted Smith to suggest a sonnet competition on the subject. Shelley's sonnet, Ozymandias, was published in The Examiner on 11 January 1818. Smith's sonnet was published on 1 February 1818.

121
James Smith (1775-1839)
Portrait by unknown artist
Oil on canvas 125.7 x 69.9 cms
NATIONAL PORTRAIT GALLERY, LONDON

In 1812, in collaboration with his brother Horace, James Smith published *Rejected Addresses*. The two brothers were well-known in London for their charm and easy wit, attainments which Shelley found attractive, but which were, for the younger poet John Keats, unappealing: after dining with Horace and James Smith in December 1817, Keats wrote to his brothers: 'They only served to convince me, how superior humour is in respect of enjoyment - These men say things which make one start, without making one feel, they are all alike; their manners are alike; they all know fashionables; they have a mannerism in their very eating & drinking, in the mere handling a Decanter -'

This portrait was probably painted in 1812, shortly after the publication of *Rejected Addresses*. In September 1812 Lord Holland, who was on the committee of Drury Lane Theatre, had invited Byron to enter the contest for an address to be delivered on the re-opening of the theatre, which had been destroyed by fire in February 1809. Over a hundred anonymous entries had previously been turned down, and the laboured mediocrity of Byron's 'winning' entry caused a public outcry and accusations of favouritism. The Smiths' *Rejected Addresses* was a series of parodies aimed at almost every living poet who might have sent in an address, including Wordsworth, Scott, Coleridge and Southey. Byron himself was amused by the parody of *Childe Harold*.

George Henry Harlow was a portrait and historical painter with strong connections with the London theatres; his portrait of Byron (entry no. 96 above) dates from 1814, when Byron joined the committee of management for Drury Lane.

Cat. 123

Cat. 122

122*
Horace & James Smith
Portrait by G. H. Harlow
c.1812
Pencil and watercolour 23 x 18 cms
JOHN MURRAY COLLECTION

123*
John Keats (1795-1821)
Portrait by Charles Armitage Brown
1819
Pencil 22.9 x 21.6 cms
NATIONAL PORTRAIT GALLERY, LONDON

Shelley and Keats would sometimes meet at Hunt's home at the Vale of Health, Hampstead, but it was a reserved and, on Keats's part, very cautious friendship. 'Keats did not take to Shelley as kindly as Shelley took to him', wrote Leigh Hunt, and Keats refused Shelley's offer to stay with him at Marlow, so that, he wrote, 'I might have my own unfettered scope.'

Oymandias by Percy Bysshe Shelley

I met a traveller from an antique land
   Who said: Two vast and trunkless legs of stone
Stand in the desart . . . Near them, on the sand,
   Half sunk, a shattered visage lies, whose frown,
And wrinkled lip, and sneer of cold command,
   Tell that its sculptor well those passions read
Which yet survive, stamped on these lifeless things,
   The hand that mocked them, and the heart that fed:
And on the pedestal these words appear:
   `My name is Ozymandias, King of Kings:
Look on My works, ye Mighty, and despair!'
   Nothing beside remains. Round the decay
Of that colossal Wreck, boundless and bare
   The lone and level sands stretch far away.

Ozymandias by Horace Smith

In Egypt's sandy silence, all alone,
   Stands a gigantic Leg, which far off throws
   The only shadow that the Desart knows:-
"I am great OZYMANDIAS," saith the stone,
   "The King of Kings; this mighty City shows
"The wonders of my hand." - The City's gone, -
   Nought but the Leg remaining to disclose
The site of this forgotten Babylon.

We wonder, - and some Hunter may express
Wonder like ours, when thro' the wilderness
   Where London stood, holding the Wolf in chace,
He meets some fragment huge, and stops to guess
   What powerful but unrecorded race
   Once dwelt in that annihilated place.

124*
John Keats (1795-1820)
Letter to Leigh Hunt.
Margate, 10 May 1817
THE BRITISH LIBRARY BOARD

At the time of Keats's writing this letter Hunt was visiting the Shelleys at Albion House in Marlow. The sheer good-humour of Keats's relation with Hunt is often overlooked - the signature is a humorous reference to the way Keats pronounced his name.

> . . . Does Shelley go on telling strange Stories of the Death of Kings? Tell him there are strange Stories of the death of Poets some have died before they were conceived 'how do you make that out Master Vellum.' Does M^rs. S. cut Bread and Butter as neatly as ever? Tell her to procure some fatal Scissors, and cut the thread of Life of all to be disappointed Poets. Does Mrs Hunt tear linen in half as straight as ever? Tell her to tear from the book of Life all blank Leaves. Remember me to them all - to Miss Kent and the little ones all.
> Your sincere friend
> John Keats alias Junkets

Hunt later printed the letter, and explained the amused reference to Shelley's story-telling as follows:

> Mr. Shelley was fond of quoting the passage here alluded to in Shakespeare, and of applying it in the most unexpected manner,
>
> > 'For God's sake let us sit upon the ground,
> > And tell strange stories of the death of kings.'
>
> Going with me to town once in the Hampstead stage, in which our only companion was an old lady, who sat silent and stiff after the English fashion, he startled her into a look of the most ludicrous astonishment by saying abruptly, 'Hunt,
>
> > For God's sake let us sit upon the ground,' &c.
>
> The old lady looked on the coach-floor, as if she expected to see us take our seats accordingly.

125*
Percy Bysshe Shelley
A Proposal for Putting Reform to the Vote throughout the Kingdom
London: C. & J. Ollier, 1817
THE BRITISH LIBRARY BOARD

Shelley puts the case for universal suffrage, but with caution: 'nothing', he concludes, 'can less consist with reason, or afford smaller hopes of any beneficial issue than the plan which should abolish the regal and the aristocratical branches of our constitution before the public mind through many gradations of improvement shall have arrived at the maturity which can disregard these symbols of it's childhood.'

126*
Percy Bysshe Shelley
Laon and Cythna; or, The Revolution of the Golden City: A Vision of the Nineteenth Century
London: C. & J. Ollier, 1818
THE BRITISH LIBRARY BOARD

𝔄 𝔓𝔯𝔬𝔭𝔬𝔰𝔞𝔩

FOR PUTTING

REFORM TO THE VOTE

THROUGHOUT THE KINGDOM.

⸻

BY THE HERMIT OF MARLOW.

⸻

LONDON:

PRINTED FOR C. AND J. OLLIER,
5, WELBECK STREET, CAVENDISH SQUARE;
By C. H. Reynell, 21, Piccadilly.

1817.

Laon and Cythna was written during the summer of 1817, and printed in the latter part of the year. When only a few copies had been issued, Ollier, the publisher, requested that certain passages be omitted or changed. Shelley reluctantly agreed to make significant alterations, particularly regarding the possibly incestuous relationship between the hero and heroine, and the revised poem was retitled *The Revolt of Islam*. Ollier's caution led to sixty-three lines of the poem being corrected. As Richard Holmes notes, only thirteen were 'cancelled because of the incest reference. The rest were cancelled because of the their controversial references to God, Hell, Christ, republicanism and atheism.

127*
Percy Bysshe Shelley
The Revolt of Islam
London: C. & J. Ollier, 1817
THE BRITISH LIBRARY BOARD

A first edition of the revised poem, with the date misprinted as 1817. 'I have trodden the glaciers of the Alps', Shelley writes in the preface to the poem, 'and lived under the eye of Mont Blanc. I have been a wanderer among distant fields. I have sailed down mighty rivers, and seen the sun rise and set, and the stars come forth, whilst I have sailed night and day down a rapid stream among mountains.' The poem is a vision of an ideal future state, rather than a

Laon and Cythna;

OR,

THE REVOLUTION

OF

THE GOLDEN CITY:

A Vision of the Nineteenth Century.

IN THE STANZA OF SPENSER.

BY

PERCY B. SHELLEY.

ΔΟΣ ΠΟΥ ΣΤΩ ΚΑΙ ΚΟΣΜΟΝ ΚΙΝΗΣΩ.
ARCHIMEDES.

LONDON:

PRINTED FOR SHERWOOD, NEELY, & JONES, PATERNOSTER-ROW; AND C. AND J. OLLIER, WELBECK-STREET:
By B. M'Millan, Bow-Street, Covent-Garden.
1818.

THE

REVOLT OF ISLAM;

A POEM,

IN TWELVE CANTOS.

BY

PERCY BYSSHE SHELLEY.

LONDON:

PRINTED FOR C. AND J. OLLIER, WELBECK-STREET;
By B M'Millan, Bow Street, Covent-Garden.
1817.

---

political statement; for the first time, Shelley denies he is writing what, as Claire Clairmont later suggested, was one of his three principle dislikes, namely didactic poetry: 'I have made no attempt to recommend the motives which I would substitute for those at present governing mankind, by methodical and systematic argument. I would only awaken the feelings, so that the reader should see the beauty of true virtue, and be incited to those enquiries which have led to my moral and political creed, and that of some of the sublimest intellects in the world. The poem therefore (with the exception of the first canto, which is purely introductory) is narrative, not didactic.' Again, the river is a constant image; the poem concludes:

The torrent of that wide and raging river
　　Is passed, and our aereal speed suspended.
We look behind; and golden mist did quiver
　　Where its wild surges with the lake were blended,-
　　Our bark hung there, as on a line suspended
Between two heavens, - that windless waveless lake
　　Which four great cataracts from four vales, attended
By mists, aye feed; from rocks and clouds they break,
And of that azure sea a silent refuge make.

Motionless resting on the lake awhile,
　　I saw its marge of snow-bright mountains rear
Their peaks aloft, I saw each radiant isle,
　　And in the midst, afar, even like a sphere
　　Hung in one hollow sky, did there appear
The temple of the Spirit; on the sound
　　Which issued thence, drawn nearer and more near,
Like the swift moon this glorious earth around,
The charmèd boat approached, and there its haven found.

Italy: 1818-1820

Exile is a state of mind as well as a physical fact. Shelley's mind was at once stimulated, and yet his poetry only subtley reflects his travelling (Livorno, Bagni di Lucca, Venice, Este, Naples, Rome and Florence); he has none of Byron's delight in new customs, historical connections and reflections upon European events. But then Shelley made it clear to Peacock that he did not like *Childe Harold*, feeling there was a perversity in its cynical undercurrents.

Shelley does perhaps pick up something from Byron that is irreplaceable. He had been privy to some of Byron's private explorations of a world of personal anxiety. It had been Byron in 1816 who was writing 'Darkness', 'Lines on hearing that Lady Byron was ill', 'The Dream', where he explored private morals in a more daring and freer way. Byron himself is the subject of Shelley's most interesting study, *Julian and Maddalo*. A friendship is celebrated, even wondered at, since the friends are of such different temperaments. But they come together over the fate of the madman, two spirits showing humanity when faced with the distress of another.

Byron's change to a new objectivity begins with his interest in drama, his first work being *Manfred*. Shelley's natural gifts pointed him to the lyrical drama of *Prometheus Unbound*, to him his most perfect composition. It had a political purpose in offering to 'the more refined classes' images of perfection which they might desire to possess for themselves. It is a mythological treatment of politics which gives them a delicate moral grandeur. Shelley's ideas about passive resistance to tyranny are articulated with a new brilliance: for instance, at the opening of Act III he suggests that every act of opposition to tryanny accumulates like flakes of snow on a mountain side until the build-up is sufficient for an avalanche to fall on all the nations around. Shelley is no longer a 'hands-on' politician, but he is striving to find the imagery by which he might affect the intellectual generation of his time. *The Cenci* does not have the profound comic vision of *Prometheus*; it is the necessary tragedy which looks at the imperfections rather than the ideals of a family. Its relation to *Prometheus* is discussed elsewhere, but it is interesting that Wordsworth was to declare it 'the greatest tragedy of the age.'

Shelley as exile still looked homeward. *Peter Bell the Third* is a further response to Wordsworth, for one remembers that *Alastor* had its origins in commenting on Wordsworthian themes. After the Shelleys had read *The Excursion* on their return from the continent in 1814, Wordsworth is declared to be 'a Slave'. In 1819, prompted by Keats's charming review of Reynolds' satiric *Peter Bell, A Lyrical Ballad*, Shelley himself attempts a satiric version that explores Wordsworth's achievement with a peculiar, knife-edged tone. He does mock, but he does not destroy; he is aware of strengths as well as weaknesses. Byron would be dismissive of Wordsworth, but Shelley was always a genuine explorer.

The other response to events in England was *The Masque of Anarchy*. This comment on the Peterloo Massacre has Shelley himself 'asleep in Italy', but no reader of 'this flaming robe of verse', as Leigh Hunt called it, could regard it as anything other than a major act, the effectual statement of revulsion against the use of force upon an unarmed public meeting.

Reviews of Shelley's work, in particular that by John Taylor Coleridge in the *Quarterly*, had their effect on Shelley. Taylor was the nephew of the poet Coleridge, and had known of Shelley's private life, from his schooldays to his first marriage. Shelley mistakenly believed the writer was Robert Southey, and he entered into a bitter exchange with the older poet. The *Quarterly*'s, review bit into Shelley's imagination and finally contributes to the central satiric attack upon reviewers in the later *Adonais* - a poem that is more given to vision than to spleen. But the unreasonable attacks by reviewers made Shelley see that this world has layers of evil which may not be compatible with the high Platonic vision to which he was committed.

very obviously hilly. By the beginning of the nineteenth century the city was impoverished and in considerable decay.

i. *Colosseum*

In the foreground are the fortressed walls of the Quatri Coronati Convent, the narrow road falling steeply towards the Colosseum.

ii. *The Temple of Concord*

The Temple of Concord immediately below the Capitol is visible behind the medieval buildings, with the Arch of Constantine in the distance.

iii. *Dome of St Peter's*

The whole palace of the Vatican is enclosed in the Leonini Walls, including the wooded section of the garden, dominated by the Dome of St Peter's.

iv. *Baths of Caracalla*

Sited in one of the most neglected of all the parts of uninhabited Rome, the sheer scale of these ruins, long since plundered for building materials, can be seen in this general view. In his preface to *Prometheus Unbound*, Shelley writes: 'This Poem was chiefly written upon the mountainous ruins of the Baths of Caracalla, among the flowery glades, the thickets of odoriferous blossom trees, which are extended in ever widening labyrinths upon its immense platforms and dizzy arches suspended in the air. The bright blue sky of Rome, and the effect of the vigorous awakening spring in that divinest climate, and the new life with which it drenches the spirits even to intoxication, were the inspiration of this drama.'

136
William Pars (1742-1782)
The Colloseum, Rome
Watercolour 38 x 54 cms
THE LAING ART GALLERY, NEWCASTLE UPON TYNE

'The Coliseum is unlike any work of human hands I ever saw before', Shelley wrote to Peacock. 'It has been changed by time into the image of an amphitheatre of rocky hills overgrown by the wild-olive the myrtle & the fig tree, & threaded by little paths which wind among its ruined stairs & immeasurable galleries; the copse-wood overshadows you as you wander through its labyrinths & the wild weeds of this climate of flowers bloom under your feet.'

137*
John Ruskin
View of the Forum of Rome
Pencil 17 x 24.8 cms
THE WORDSWORTH TRUST

On 23 March 1819 Shelley wrote to Peacock:

'The ruins of the antient Forum are so far fortunate that they have not been walled up in the modern city. They stand in an open lonesome plain, bounded on one side by the modern city & the other by the Palatine Mount covered with shapeless masses of ruin. The tourists tell you all about these things, & I am afraid of stumbling upon their language when I enumerate what is so well known. There remain eight granite columns of the Ionic order with their tableture of the Temple of Concord founded by Camillus; I fear that the immense expense demanded by these columns forbids us to hope that they are the remains of any edifice dedicated by that most perfect & virtuous of men. It is supposed to have been repaired under the earlier Emperors; alas, what a contrast of recollections.'

T H E   C E N C I.

A   T R A G E D Y,

IN FIVE ACTS.

By P E R C Y   B.   S H E L L E Y.

I T A L Y.
PRINTED FOR C. AND J. OLLIER
VERE STREET, BOND STREET.
L O N D O N.
1819.

138*
Percy Bysshe Shelley
The Cenci
London: C. & J. Ollier, 1819
THE BRITISH LIBRARY BOARD

Shelley possessed a print of the beautiful original of his heroine, Beatrice Cenci, based on her portrait attributed to Guido Reni. Virtuous as Beatrice was, when faced with a world governed by male tyranny (incestuous father, the Pope and God himself), Shelley sees her as condemned because of her participation in her father's death. Her complicity in murder amounted to 'self-contempt'. To Shelley, virtue was an internal power of the mind. In a world where progress was inevitable, (called by Godwin and Shelley 'Necessity') the proper moral stance was one of wise passivity.

Shelley wrote *The Cenci* between the idealistic conclusion to the third act of *Prometheus Unbound* and the celebratory fourth act. It offers a dark look at the destructive forces within a family, especially perilous when society supports a tyrannous male domination.

Cat. 140

140
Julia Margaret Cameron
Beatrice
19 October 1870
Photograph: albumen print
Lincolnshire County Council:
Tennyson Research Centre, Lincoln

The celebrated Victorian photographer, Julia Margaret Cameron has based her study of Beatrice on the model of the portrait attributed to Guido Reni. The *Cenci* went through numerous editions during the second half of the nineteenth century.

Cat. 139

139*
Maria Anna Cenci
Engraving by L. Legoux after a follower of Guido Reni
Published 25 April 1794
Stipple engraving 20 x 15 cms
David Alexander Collection

The engraving is misleadingly entitled 'Maria Anna Cenci'. It is based on a popular painting of Beatrice Cenci once thought to be by Guido Reni, a copy of which hung on the wall of Shelley's room in Rome. 'There is a fixed and pale composure upon the features', he wrote, 'The moulding of her face is exquisitely delicate; the eyebrows are distinct and arched; lips have that permanent meaning of imagination and sensibility which suffering has not repressed. ... Her forehead is large and clear; her eyes, which we are told were remarkable for their vivacity, are swollen with weeping and lustreless, but beautifully tender and serene. ... Beatrice Cenci appears to have been one of those rare persons in whom energy and gentleness dwelt together without destroying one another.'

141*
Percy Bysshe Shelley
Prometheus Unbound. A Lyrical Drama
London: C. & J. Ollier, 1820
Private Collection [The British Library Board]

Prometheus Unbound was begun at Este in October 1818 (Act One); continued at Rome in March and April 1819 (Acts Two and Three) and concluded at Florence in late 1819 (Act Four). In his illuminating Preface Shelley declares it 'a mistake to suppose that I dedicate my poetical compositions solely to direct enforcement of reform' . Though in some ways he was always a teacher, Shelley was pre-eminently a poet and could declare truthfully, 'Didactic poetry is my abhorrence'. His real gift was to make his readers aware of the human potential:

My purpose has hitherto been simply to familiarise the highly refined imagination of the more select classes of poetical readers with beautiful idealisms of moral excellence; aware that until the mind can love, and admire, and trust, and hope, and endure, reasoned principles of

PROMETHEUS UNBOUND

A LYRICAL DRAMA

IN FOUR ACTS

WITH OTHER POEMS

BY

PERCY BYSSHE SHELLEY

AUDISNE HÆC, AMPHIARAE, SUB TERRAM ABDITE?

LONDON
C AND J OLLIER VERE STREET BOND STREET
1820

moral conduct are seeds cast upon the highway of life which the unconscious passenger tramples into dust, although they would bear the harvest of his happiness. Should I live to accomplish what I purpose, that is, produce a systematical history of what appear to me to be the genuine elements of human society, let not the advocates of injustice flatter themselves that I should take Aeschylus rather than Plato as my model.

Shelley's lyric drama can happily be paralleled with Beethoven's opera *Fidelio*, written some ten years earlier; for both poet and composer, the principle of active love is embodied in the feminine, the wife. It is the woman's energy of love that can release the imprisoned masculine strength. But both need the enabling force of Demogorgon, the 'necessary' forward principle, the inevitable impulse for change and progress. It is that tendency that is found at the centre of the earth, whither Asia travels, and where Demogorgon is found.

142*
Percy Bysshe Shelley
Portrait after A. Curran
Oil on ivory H 13 cms
LORD ABINGER COLLECTION

Amelia Curran, a close friend of the Shelleys in Rome, started a portait of Shelley in 1819, but was dissatisfied with it and threw it aside. At Mary Shelley's request, she finished it after Shelley's death. Romanticised versions of the portrait such as this one were popular in the years following Shelley's death.

143*
Percy Bysshe Shelley
Portrait by Alfred Clint after Amelia Curran and Edward Ellerker Williams
Oil on canvas 59.7 x 49.5 cms
THE NATIONAL PORTRAIT GALLERY

This portrait by Clint was 'composed' from the Curran portrait, a watercolour by Edward Williams, and the oral suggestions and descriptions from Jane Williams and Mary Shelley.

144
Percy Bysshe Shelley
Letter to Thomas Love Peacock
Livorno, [24] August 1819
THE BRITISH LIBRARY BOARD

This letter, with its reminiscences of Windsor and the Thames, shows that, although he was never to return from the Continent, Shelley's thoughts were frequently of England:

My dear Peacock,
I ought first to say that I have not yet received one of your letters from Naples, - in Italy such things are difficult - but your present letter tells me all that I could desire to hear of your situation.

My employments are these, I awaken usually at 7. read half an hour, then get up, breakfast. After breakfast *ascend my tower*, and read or write until two. Then we dine - after dinner I read Dante with Mary, gossip a little, eat grapes & figs, sometimes walk, though seldom; and at 1/2 past 5. pay a visit to Mrs Gisborne who reads Spanish with me until near seven. We then come for Mary & stroll about till suppertime. Mrs Gisborne is a sufficiently amiable & very accomplished woman she is δημοκρατικη & αθεη [democratic and atheistic] - how far she may be φιλανθρωπη [philanthropic] I dont know for she is the antipodes of enthusiasm. Her husband a man with little thin lips receding forehead & a prodigious nose is an excessive bore. His nose is something quite Slawkenburgian - it weighs on the imagination to look at it, - it is that sort of nose which transforms all the *g*s its wearer utters into *k*s. It is a nose once seen never to be forgotten and which requires the utmost stretch of Christian charity to forgive. I, you know, have a little turn up nose; Hogg has a large hook one but add them both together, square them, cube them, you would have but a faint idea of the nose to which I refer.

I most devoutly wish that I were living near London. - I dont think I shall settle so far off as Richmond, & to inhabit any intermediate spot on the Thames would be to expose myself to the river damps, not to mention that it is not much to my taste - My inclinations point to Hampstead, but I dont know whether I should not make up my mind to something more completely suburban. What are mountains trees heaths, or even the glorious & ever beautiful sky with such sunsets as I have seen at Hampstead to friends? Social employment in some form or other is the alpha & the omega of existence.

All that I see in Italy - and from my tower window I now see the magnificent peaks of the Apennine half enclosing the plain - is nothing - it dwindles to smoke in the mind, when I think of some familiar forms of

Cat. 145

scenery little perhaps in themselves over which old remembrances have thrown a delightful colour. How we prize what we despised when present! So the ghosts of our dead associations rise & haunt us in revenge for our having let them starve, & abandoned them to perish.

You dont tell me if you see the Boinvilles, nor are they included in the list of the conviti at the monthly symposium. I will attend it in imagination.

One thing I own I am curious about - and in the chance of the letters not coming from Naples, pray tell me. - *What* is it you do at the India House? Hunt writes and says, you have got a *situation* in the India House - Hogg that you have a *honourable employment* - Godwin writes to Mary that you have got so *much or so much*, - but nothing of what you *do*. The Devil take these general terms, not content with having driven all poetry out [of] the world, at length they make war upon their own allies, nay their very parents - dry facts. If it had not been the age of generalities any one of these people would have told me what *you did*.

I have been much better these last three weeks - my work on the Cenci, which was done in two months, was a fine antidote to nervous medicines & kept up, I think, the pain in my side, as sticks do a fire. Since then I have materially improved. I do not walk enough. Clare who is sometimes my companion, sometimes does not dress in exactly the right time. - I have no stimulus to walk. Now, I go sometimes to Livorno on business & that does me good.

England seems to be in a very disturbed state, if we may judg[e b]y some Paris Papers. I suspect it is rather overrated, but when I hear them talk of paying in gold - nay I dare say take steps towards it, confess that the sinking fund is a fraud &c. I no longer wonder. But the change should commence among the higher orders, or anarchy will only be the last flash before despotism. I wonder & tremble, - *You* are well sheltered in the East India Co[mpan]y. No change could possibly touch you.

I have been reading Calderon in Spanish - a kind of Shakespeare is this Calderon, & I have some thoughts, if I find that I cannot do anything better, of translating some of his plays. - and some Greek ones besides. - but my head is full of all sorts of plans.

The Examiners I receive. - Hunt as a political writer pleases me more & more. - Adieu - Mary & Clare send their best remembrances.
Your most faithful friend
P B Shelley

[P.S.] Pray send me some books and Clare would take it as a great favour if you would send her *music books*.

145*
Unknown artist
The Peterloo Massacre
Published by Richard Carlile, 1 October 1819
Engraving 32 x 46.5 cms
THE WORDSWORTH TRUST

On 16 August 1819, at St Peter's Field, on the outskirts of Manchester, a large public meeting was dispersed by dragoon guards, with a brutality that left several people dead. When Shelley heard the news from Florence, he wrote to his publisher Ollier: 'the same day that your letter came, came news of the Manchester work, & the torrent of my indignation has not yet done wailing in my veins. I await anx-

The Masque of Anarchy

As I lay asleep in Italy
There came a voice from over the Sea,
And with great power it forth led me
To walk in the visions of Poesy.

I met murder on the way -
He had a mask like Castlereagh -
Very smooth he looked, yet grim;
Seven blood-hounds followed him:

All were fat; and well they might
Be in admirable plight,
For one by one, and two by two,
He tossed them human hearts to chew
Which from his wide cloak he drew.

Next came Fraud, and he had on,
Like Eldon, an ermined gown;
His big tears, for he wept well,
Turned to mill-stones as they fell.

And the little children, who
Round his feet played to and fro,
Thinking every tear a gem,
Had their brains knocked out by them.

Clothed with the Bible, as with light,
And the shadows of the night,
Like Sidmouth, next, Hypocrisy
On a crocodile rode by.

And many more Destructions played
In this ghastly masquerade,
All disguised, even to the eyes,
Like Bishops, lawyers, peers, or spies.

Last came Anarchy: he rode
On a white horse, splashed with blood;
He was pale even to the lips,
Like Death in the Apocalypse.

And he wore a kingly crown;
And in the grasp a sceptre shone;
On his brow this mark I saw -
'I AM GOD, AND KING, AND LAW!'

With a pace stately and fast,
Over English land he passed,
Trampling to a mire of blood
The adoring multitude.

And a mighty troop around,
With their trampling shook the ground,
Waving each a bloody sword,
For the services of their Lord.

And with glorious triumph, they
Rode through England proud and gay,
Drunk as with intoxication
Of the wine of desolation.

O'er fields and towns, from sea to sea,
Passed the Pageant swift and free,
Tearing up, and trampling down;
Till they came to London town.

And each dweller, panic-stricken,
Felt his heart with terror sicken
Hearing the tempestuous cry
Of the triumph of Anarchy.

For with pomp to meet him came,
Clothed in arms like blood and flame,
The hired murderers, who did sing
'Thou art God, and Law, and King.

'We have waited, weak and lone
For thy coming, Mighty One!
Our purses are empty, our swords are cold,
Give us glory, and blood, and gold.'

Lawyers and priests, a motley crowd,
To the earth their pale brows bowed;
Like a bad prayer not over loud,
Whispering - 'Thou are Law and God'.' -

Then all cried with one accord,
'Thou art King, and God, and Lord;
Anarchy, to thee we bow,
Be thy name made holy now!'

And Anarchy, the Skeleton,
Bowed and grinned to every one,
As well as if his education
Had cost ten millions to the nation.

For he knew the Palaces
Of our Kings were rightly his;
His the sceptre, crown, and globe,
And the gold-inwoven robe.

(Stanzas 1-20)

iously to hear how the Country will express its sense of this bloody murderous oppression of its destroyers.' His own response was his poem *The Masque of Anarchy*, written at white heat as soon as he heard the news, but not published in England until 1832.

The publisher and free thinker, Richard Carlile, addresses this print to Henry Hunt, the orator at the meeting. The prominence that it gives to the figure of Women's Suffrage is unusual.

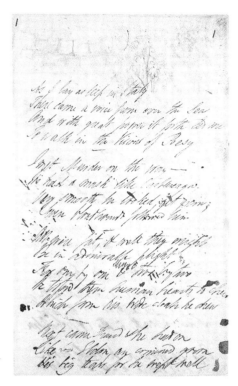

Cat. 146

146*
Percy Bysshe Shelley
The Masque of Anarchy
1819
THE BRITISH LIBRARY BOARD

Leigh Hunt, the editor of *The Examiner*, thought it imprudent to publish *The Masque of Anarchy*, though he had it by 23 September 1819. Thus, as a weapon of the moment the poem must be deemed ineffectual (it was not published until 1832, the year of the great reform act), but its indignant satire is still effective, its icy contempt for those who wield brutal repression rising, within a fantastic allegorical framework.

147*
Percy Bysshe Shelley
The Masque of Anarchy
London: Edward Moxon, 1832
THE BRITISH LIBRARY BOARD

Leigh Hunt comments in the preface:

> I did not insert it [in 1819] because I thought that the public at large had not become sufficiently discerning to do justice to the sincerity and kind-heartedness of the spirit that walked in this flaming robe of verse.

148
Leigh Hunt
The Literary Pocket-Book; or, Companion for the Lover of Nature and Art
London: C. & J. Ollier, 1819
ETON SCHOOL COLLECTION

'I have been writing a *Pocket-Book*', wrote Leigh Hunt to the Shelleys on 12 November 1818, 'It is entitled the 'Literary Pocket-Book, or Companion for the Lover of Art and Nature,' and contains a long calendar of the months, written by myself, interspersed with quotations from dead and *living* poets; lists of men of original genius from the earliest times to the present'. The book contained Shelley's 1817 poem 'Marianne's Dream', as well as two sonnets by Keats. Shelley's opinion of this work is not recorded, but, in England, Keats was less than admiring - '[Hunt] has lately publish'd a Pocket-Book called the literary Pocket-Book', he wrote to George and Georgiana Keats in December 1818, 'full of the most sickening stuff you can imagine.'

This copy is inscribed on the inside cover: 'Sophia Stacy given her by Percy Bysshe Shelley Florence Desbr 29th 1820 Italy. Bysshe Shelley was drowned near Lerici Italy with his friend Mr Williams in 1823 [sic]'. Sophia Stacey was the ward of one of Shelley's uncles. On the Grand Tour, accompanied by her elderly chaperone, Miss Corbet Parry-Jones, she paid a formal visit to the Shelleys. Shelley's notoriety - atheist, womaniser and poet - attracted Sophia and appalled Miss Parry-Jones. Shelley's charm subsequently overcame them both.

149
Euripides
Tragoediae
Oxford: N. Bliss, 1811
ETON COLLEGE COLLECTION

These faint and hurried phrasings scribbled on the back fly-leaf of this pocket-sized book seem allied to one of Shelley's greatest poems, *Ode to the West Wind*. Shelley's theme there is that the dramatic change caused by the Autumn is a natural principle in all things. For Shelley, 'change' was the permanent aspect of nature. The poem's power is in part in the epic scale of its imagery; its imperative voice measures a power which is calling on the wind to fulfil its epic mission. At its climax the poem becomes a prayer that the poet and the wind should be one. By this point the wind is political as well as natural.

Ode to the West Wind

O wild West Wind, thou breath of Autumn's being,
Thou, from whose unseen presence the leaves dead
Are driven, like ghosts from an enchanter fleeing,

Yellow, and black, and pale, and hectic red,
Pestilence-stricken multitudes: O Thou,
Who chariotest to their dark wintry bed

The winged seeds, where they lie cold and low,
Each like a corpse within its grave, until
Thine azure sister of the Spring shall blow

Her clarion o'er the dreaming earth, and fill
(Driving sweet buds like flocks to feed in air)
With living hues and odours plain and hill:

Wild Spirit, which art moving everywhere;
Destroyer and Preserver; hear, O hear!

II

Thou on whose stream, 'mid the steep sky's commotion,
Loose clouds like Earth's decaying leaves are shed,
Shook from the tangled boughs of Heaven and Ocean,

Angels of rain and lightning: there are spread
On the blue surface of thine aery surge,
Like the bright hair uplifted from the head

Of some fierce Maenad, even from the dim verge
Of the horizon to the zenith's height,
The locks of the approaching storm. Thou Dirge

Of the dying year, to which this closing night
Will be the dome of a vast sepulchre,
Vaulted with all thy congregated might

Of vapours, from whose solid atmosphere
Black rain and fire and hail will burst: O hear!

III

Thou who didst waken from his summer dreams
The blue Mediterranean, where he lay,
Lulled by the coil of his chrystalline streams,

Beside a pumice isle in Baiae's bay,
And saw in sleep old palaces and towers
Quivering within the wave's intenser day,

All overgrown with azure moss and flowers
So sweet, the sense faints picturing them! Thou
For whose path the Atlantic's level powers

Cleave themselves into chasms, while far below
The sea-blooms and the oozy woods which wear
The sapless foliage of the ocean, know

Thy voice, and suddenly grow grey with fear,
And tremble and despoil themselves: O hear!

IV

If I were a dead leaf thou mightest bear;
If I were a swift cloud to fly with thee;
A wave to pant beneath thy power, and share

The impulse of thy strength, only less free
Than thou, O Uncontrollable! If even
I were as in my boyhood, and could be

The comrade of thy wanderings over Heaven,
As then, when to outstrip thy skiey speed
Scarce seemed a vision; I would ne'er have striven

As thus with thee in prayer, in my sore need.
Oh! lift me as a wave, a leaf, a cloud!
I fall upon the thorns of life! I bleed!

A heavy weight of hours has chained and bowed
One too like thee: tameless, and swift, and proud.

V

Make me thy lyre, even as the forest is:
What if my leaves are falling like its own!
The tumult of thy mighty harmonies

Will take from both a deep, autumnal tone,
Sweet though in sadness. Be thou, Spirit fierce,
My spirit! Be thou me, impetuous one!

Drive my dead thoughts over the universe
Like withered leaves to quicken a new birth!
And, by the incantation of this verse,

Scatter, as from an unextinguished hearth
Ashes and sparks, my words among mankind!
Be through my lips to unawakened Earth

The trumpet of a prophecy! O Wind,
If Winter comes, can Spring be far behind?

Pisa: 1820-1822

The Shelleys' arrival at Pisa early in 1820 was to be a green island in their wandering life. 'We are tired of roving' wrote Mary. The only child to survive Shelley, Percy Florence, was now two months old, and having lost two of their children in Italy, William and Clara, Pisa had the advantage that Vacca Berlingheri, the distinguished physician, was a professor at the University. Their introduction into Pisan society was made possible by their early acquaintance with Mr and Mrs Mason, alias George Tighe and Lady Mount Cashell. Mary found some English society more necessary than Shelley did. He himself was attentive to Claire Clairmont, was concerned about her relations with Byron, and sympathetic over her unhappiness about Byron's treatment of Allegra. When Shelley finally persuaded Byron to come with Teresa Guiccioli to Pisa, they were to live on opposite sides of the Arno, each house within sight of the other.

There then began the society with riding, shooting and boating trips, an idyll much marred by the drama of the absurd but potentially dangerous quarrel with one of the local dragoons. Reading and writing were the Shelleys' main activities. Three works of major importance were written. The first was *Epipsychidion*, published anonymously in May 1821. This treatment of ideal love based on Shelley's encounter with the beautiful daughter of the governor of Pisa, Emilia Viviani, meant that the politics of marriage was one of Shelley's real concerns. It is not a poem with a programme, but is an exploration of human possibilities. The second great work was the *Defence of Poetry*, written in response to an attack by his friend Peacock. Shelley's defence of poetry and of poets as 'the unacknowledged legislators of the world' is a primary text for all critical discussions about the nature of poetry. Finally, *Adonais* was written to mark the death of John Keats. It is one of the great English elegies, the better for Shelley's knowledge of the Greek sources, and the more powerful because of the Platonic speculations he is able to include (especially the difficulty with the 'otherness' of the Platonic ideals); and the more moving for its confession of his possible failure as a poet in pursuit of the ideal with which the poem so emphatically concludes.

The arrival of the Greek leader, Prince Mavrocordatos brought the active politics of the Greek independence movement into their lives. Shelley's dramatic poem *Hellas*, dedicated to the prince, was one result. Another was the attention that both Shelley, but especially Byron, were to receive from the authorities. But his other explorations were about the nature of poetry itself, in his witty and astonishing *The Witch of Atlas*. His dexterity with form allowed him to imitate a Greek satyr play in his *Swellfoot the Tyrant*, a poem of satiric bathos, commenting on the Queen Caroline affair in England.

By happy accident, Shelley's cousin Thomas Medwin joined them at Pisa, and introduced him to the Cornish adventurer Edward John Trelawny, and to Edward and Jane Williams, the Shelleys' last intimate friends. Shelley's distaste for Byron's society grew - fed perhaps by too much Byronic hauteur, too much actual inequality, too much popular success for Byron's poetry. Shelley decided to move north to San Terenzo, near Lerici on the Gulf of Spezia.

Cat. 150

150*
T. Higham after J.D. Harding
Pisa
Published by John Murray, London 1833
Line engraving 8.5 x 12.9 cms
PRIVATE COLLECTION [THE BRITISH LIBRARY BOARD]

151*
Percy Bysshe Shelley
Oedipus Tyrannus; or, Swellfoot the Tyrant
London: J. Johnston, 1820
THE BRITISH LIBRARY BOARD

Shelley's mock tragedy is a reckless fantasy alluding to George IV's decision to put Queen Caroline on trial rather than accept her as his consort. According to Mary Shelley, the poem was first conceived when Shelley was staying at Casa Prinni in San Giuliano, his cooler residence outside Pisa; Shelley tried to read aloud his 'Ode to Liberty' and found the noise of squealing pigs overwhelming. Hence the beast fable element in Shelley's tale, where the pigs are slaughtered or gelded (a farcical solution to Malthus and his fears of over-population).

152*
Percy Bysshe Shelley
Epipsychidion
London: C. & J. Ollier, 1821
THE BRITISH LIBRARY BOARD

Shelley writes in the *Defence of Poetry*: 'The freedom of women produced the poetry of sexual love. Love became a religion the idols of whose worship were ever present.... The true relation borne to each other by the sexes into which human kind is distributed has become less misunderstood; and if the error which confounded diversity with inequality of the power of the two sexes has been partially recognized in the opinions and institutions of modern Europe, we owe this great benefit to the worship of which chivalry was the law, and poets the prophets'.

Robert Frost, the American poet, was to declare that his reading of *Epipsychidion* changed his life by changing his idea of love. The poem is critical of conventional marriage, which is described as 'The dreariest and the longest journey', and goes on to explore the experience of free love. It is not about sexual triumph; rather it is Shelley's honest and delicate attempt to describe feelings of tenderness to three women in his life at one given moment. As he told his friend John Gisborne: 'if you are anxious, however, to hear what I am and have been, it will tell you something thereof. It is an idealized history of my life and feelings'. Shelley refers to his wife Mary as the moon, to Claire Clairmont as the comet, and to Teresa Viviani (called 'Emily' in the poem) as the sun. For Shelley, Emily is much like Dante's Beatrice, real and ideal at the same time. In reality 'Emily' was the daughter of the governor of Pisa, and was kept in a convent while awaiting arrangements for her marriage. Shelley's final paeon in praise of Emily is a testament to the power of love; he creates in words an ideal setting (a Greek island) and an ideal relation-

ŒDIPUS TYRANNUS;

OR,

SWELLFOOT *the* TYRANT.

A Tragedy.

IN TWO ACTS.

TRANSLATED FROM THE ORIGINAL DORIC.

———— Choose Reform or civil-war,
When thro' thy streets, instead of hare with dogs,
A Consort-Queen shall hunt a King with hogs,
Riding on the IONIAN MINOTAUR.

LONDON ·
PUBLISHED FOR THE AUTHOR,
BY J. JOHNSTON, 98, CHEAPSIDE, AND SOLD BY
ALL BOOKSELLERS.
1820.

EPIPSYCHIDION :

VERSES ADDRESSED TO THE NOBLE

AND UNFORTUNATE LADY

EMILIA V————

NOW IMPRISONED IN THE CONVENT OF ——

L'anima amante si slancia fuori del creato, e si crea nel infinito
un Mondo tutto per essa, diverso assai da questo oscuro e pauroso
baratro. HER OWN WORDS.

LONDON
C AND J OLLIER VERE STREET BOND STREET
MDCCCXXI.

---

ship. The poem however concludes with a collapse of language and some awareness that what has been envisaged has value but, alas, is not sustainable. Here, as elsewhere, Shelley's exploration into human feeling is radical; he dramatizes desires and states of mind that are almost taboo, and this one reason why we are drawn to him.

153*
Percy Bysshe Shelley
Hellas, A Lyrical Drama
London: Charles & James Ollier, 1822
THE BRITISH LIBRARY BOARD

At Pisa in December 1820 Shelley met Prince Alexandros Mavrocordatos, a leader in the cause of Greek independence from Turkish domination. Less than a year later, in October 1821, six months after the War of Greek Independence had begun, he wrote his play, based upon *The Persians* of Aeschylus, and dedicated it to Mavrocordatos. Shelley's optimism was based on an ideal view of the war. If Shelley had lived, he would, like Byron, have sought in practical ways to help to set Greece free.

HELLAS

A LYRICAL DRAMA

BY

PERCY B. SHELLEY

ΜΑΝΤΙΣ ΕΙΜ' ΕΣΘΛΩΝ ΑΓΩΝΩΝ
ŒDIP. COLON.

LONDON

CHARLES AND JAMES OLLIER VERE STREET
BOND STREET
MDCCCXXII

154*
Marianne Hunt (engr. S. Freeman)
*Lord Byron as he Appeared After His Daily Ride at
Pisa & Genoa*
6 October 1826
Engraving 29.5 x 21.5 cms
NEWSTEAD ABBEY

Below the silhouette is the following quotation:

He used to sit in this manner out of doors with the back
of the chair for an arm, his body indolently bent, and his
face turned gently upwards, often with an expression of
doubt and disdain about the mouth. His riding dress was
a mazarine blue camlet frock, with a cape, a velvet cap
of the same colour lined with green, with a gold band
and tassel and black shade; and trowsers, waistcoat and
gaters all white and of one material. The cap had
something of the look of a coronet, and was a little
pulled forward over the shade. His lame foot (the left)
but slightly affected his general appearance; it was a
shrunken, not a club foot, was turned a little on one side,
and hurt him if much walked upon, but as he lounged
about a room the defect was hardly observable. The rest
of his person till he grew fat was eminently handsome;
so were his mouth and chin fit for a bust of Apollo. The
fault of the face was that the jaws were too wide
compared with the temples, and the eyes too near one
another. Latterly he grew thin again, as he was in
England. His hair had been thick and curling, but was
rapidly falling off. The above likeness is believed to be
the only genuine one of the noble Poet ever taken at full
length. It was recognized by those who knew his Lordship in Italy, with that laughter of delight common
upon seeing the expression as well as features happily
caught, and it is but justice to the able Engraver (who
was kind enough to undertake a work apparently very
easy, but in reality far from it,) to say, that he has been
equally happy in transferring it to the Copper.

155
Countess Teresa Guiccioli (1799-1873)
Portrait by Henry William Pickersgill
1832 (finished 1869-70)
Oil on canvas 122 x 97 cms
PRIVATE COLLECTION

Teresa Guiccioli was Byron's mistress from 1819
until his death, and was one of the Shelley-Byron
circle at Pisa. 'Shelley seemed more Spirit than man'
is the conclusion to her vivid account of him in her
memoirs. To Shelley she was Byron's 'good Angel
who led him from darkness to light'. In a letter to
John Gisborne, 22 October 1821, Shelley is less
polite: 'La Guiccioli his cara sposa who attends him
impatiently, is a very pretty sentimental [stupid
deleted] innocent, superficial Italian, who has sacrificed
an immense fortune to live [with *deleted*] for Lord
Byron; and who, if I know anything of my friend of
her, or of human nature will hereafter have plenty of
leisure & opportunity to repent of her rashness. -
Lord B. is however quite cured of his gross habits - as
far as habits - the perverse ideas on which they were
founded are not yet eradicated.' She first visited
England in 1832.

Cat. 155

156*
Percy Bysshe Shelley
Letter to Lord Byron
Pisa, 21 October 1821
THE BRITISH LIBRARY BOARD

Shelley was the only great poet whom Byron knew
intimately. His support for *Don Juan* was unreserved
and helped Byron to continue it against attacks from
both friend and foe:

My dear Lord Byron
    I should have written to you long since but that I
have been led to expect you almost daily in Pisa, & that
I imagined you would cross my letter on your road.
Many thanks for Don Juan It is a poem totally of its own
species, & my wonder and delight at the grace of the
composition no less than the free & grand vigour of the
conception of it perpetually increase. The few passages
which any one might desire to be cancelled in the 1st &
2d Cantos are here reduced almost to nothing. This
poem carries with it at once the stamp of originality and
a defiance of imitation. Nothing has ever been written
like it in English nor if I may venture to prophesy, will
there be; without carrying upon it the mark of a
secondary and borrowed light. You unveil & present in
its true deformity what is worst in human nature, & this
is what the witlings of the age murmur at, conscious of
their want of power to endure the scrutiny of such a
light. We are damned to the knowledge of good & evil,
and it is [good *cancelled*] well for us to know what we
should avoid no less than what we should seek. The
character of Lambro his return the merriment of his
daughters guests made as it were in celebration of his
funeral the meeting with the lovers and the death of
Haidée, are circumstances combined & developed in a
manner that I seek elsewhere in vain. The fifth canto,
which some of your pet Zoili in Albemarle St. said was
dull, gathers instead of loses, splendour & energy the

language in which the whole is clothed a sort of c[h]ameleon under the changing sky of the spirit that kindles it is such as these lisping days could not have expected, and are, believe me, in spite of the approbation which you wrest from them little pleased to hear. One can hardly judge from recitation and it was not until I read it in print that I have been able to do it justice. This sort of writing only on a great plan & perhaps in a more compact form is what I wished you to do when I made my vows for an epic. But I am content You are building up a drama, such as England has not yet seen, and the task is sufficiently noble & worthy of you.

When may we expect you? The Countess G[uiccioli] is very patient, though sometimes she seems apprehensive that you will *never* leave Ravenna. I have suffered from my habitual disorder & from a tertian fever since I returned, & my ill health has prevented me from shewing her the attentions I could have desired in Pisa. I have heard from Hunt, who tells me that he is coming out in November, by sea I believe Your house is ready & all the furniture arranged. Lega they say is to have set off yesterday The Countess tells me that you think of leaving Allegra for the present at the convent. Do as you think best but I can pledge myself to find a situation for her here such as you would approve, in case you change your mind.

I hear no political news but such as announces the slow victory of the spirit of the past over that of the present. The other day a number of Heteristi, escaped from the defeat in Wallachia, past through Pisa, to embark at Leghorn & join Ipsilanti in Livadia. It is highly to the credit of the actual government of Tuscany, that it allowed these brave fugitives 3 livres a day each, & free quarters during their passage through these states. Mrs. S[helley] desires her best regards.
My dear Lord Byron
Yours most faithfully
P.B. Shelley

157*
Lord Byron
Don Juan, Cantos 6 & 7
1822
THE BRITISH LIBRARY BOARD

At the beginning of Canto 7 Byron allows his hero to escape from the Turkish harem in Constantinople to fight on the Russian side in the Russo-Turkish wars. His account is one of the first 'anti-war' poems. Byron's satirical contempt for the 'heroic' slaughter is typically enough put beside one optimistic image - amid the carnage Juan and his English friend Johnson rescue a child.

158
Lord Byron
Don Juan, Cantos 6, 7 & 8
1822
Transcribed by Mary Shelley
JOHN MURRAY COLLECTION

The manuscript is open to show Canto 8, stanzas 5-13. Mary continued with her fair copy in Genoa after Shelley's death in 1822. The note at the top right

hand is copied out by Mary from Byron's rough draft: Byron feels it necessary, on looking over her fair copy, to add another note making clear that his attack is against Wordsworth's, to Byron, outrageous claim that the slaughter at the Battle of Waterloo was, Wordsworth wrote, part of the divine plan: 'Yea, carnage is thy daughter'. Byron originally wrote: 'To wit, the Deities'. He then adds to Mary's copy: 'This is perhaps as pretty a pedigree for murder - as ever was found out by Garter King at Arms. What would have been said had any of us free-spoken people discovered such a lineage?'

Cat. 159 (*Don Juan* Canto 1, 181)

159
Richard Westall (1765-1836)
Eleven illustrations to the works of Lord Byron
Watercolour 12 x 10 cms
JOHN MURRAY COLLECTION

160
Edward John Trelawny (1792-1881)
Portrait by Brian Duppa
Signed and Inscribed
Pencil 17.1 x 10.2 cms
NATIONAL PORTRAIT GALLERY, LONDON

Edward John Trelawny, Cornishman and adventurer, met Shelley the day he arrived at Pisa, 14 January 1822. Mary Shelley gives a detailed description of him in her journal:

Trelawney is extravagant ... partly natural and partly perhaps put on, but it suits him well, and if his abrupt but not unpolished manners be assumed, they are nevertheless in unison with his Moorish face (for he looks

Cat. 161

Oriental yet not Asiatic) his dark hair, his Herculean form, and then there is an air of extreme good nature which pervades his whole countenance, especially when he smiles, which assures me that his heart is good.

161*
Edward John Trelawny (1792-1881)
Portrait by Joseph Severn
Signed and Dated 1838
Pen and ink 15.2 x 15.2 cms
NATIONAL PORTRAIT GALLERY, LONDON

162*
Edward Ellerker Williams
Diary
21 October - 11 July 1822
THE BRITISH LIBRARY BOARD

Recovered from Williams's body after his death, the diary is in parts badly faded. In this extract, dated Monday, May 6, Williams recounts one of Shelley's waking visions:

> After tea, walking with Shelley on the terrace, and observing the effect of moonshine on the waters, he complained of being unusually nervous, and stopping short he grasped me violently by the arm, and stared steadfastly on the white surf that broke upon the beach under our feet. Observing him sensibly affected, I demanded of him if he were in pain? But he only answered by saying, "There it is again - There!" He recovered after some time, and declared he saw, as plainly as he then saw me, a naked child (the child of a

friend who had lately died) rise from the sea and clap its hands as in joy, smiling at him.

163*
Percy Bysshe Shelley
To Jane - The Recollection
2 February 1822
THE BRITISH LIBRARY BOARD

Edward and Jane Williams, friends of Thomas Medwin, became intimate with the Shelleys at Pisa early in 1821. Some of Shelley's finest lyrics are addressed to Jane.

164*
Percy Bysshe Shelley
'When the lamp is shattered'
THE BRITISH LIBRARY BOARD

A late lyric written to Jane Williams.

165*
Thomas Medwin (1788-1869)
Miniature by unknown artist
Watercolour H 6 cms
DAVID GARDNER-MEDWIN COLLECTION

Medwin, a cousin and old school-friend, joined Shelley in Pisa in October 1820, shortly after Lord Byron, and introduced Shelley to Trelawny and Edward Williams (like himself retired on half pay from the 8th Dragoons of the East India Company. He was a somewhat reckless, even a naive chronicler of both Byron and Shelley.

Cat. 165

Cat. 145 Unknown artist, *The Peterloo Massacre*

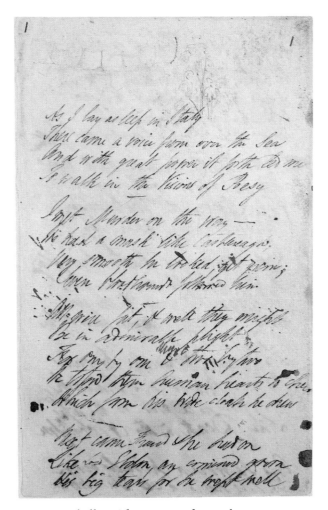

Cat. 146 Shelley, *The Masque of Anarchy*

Cat. 183 Louis-Eduard Fournier, *Shelley's Funeral Rites*

Cat. 184 W.B. Morris, *Keats' Grave and the Pyramid of Cestius*

166*
John Keats
Poems
London: C. & J. Ollier, 1817
PRIVATE COLLECTION [THE BRITISH LIBRARY BOARD]

Keats's first collection of poetry, including 'Sleep and Poetry', 'I stood tip-toe upon a little hill' and the sonnet 'On First Looking into Chapman's Homer'. The poems are not all distinguished, and Shelley had, when walking on Hampstead Heath with Keats in the autumn of 1816, advised the younger author to delay publication until he could produce a better collection.

167*
John Keats
Endymion: A Poetic Romance
London: Taylor & Hessey, 1818
PRIVATE COLLECTION [THE BRITISH LIBRARY BOARD]

Keats's second publication, a long poem in blank verse, seems to have been written in friendly competition with Shelley, who produced *The Revolt of Islam*. Shelley was more admiring but still reserved. In a letter to Charles Ollier, 6 September 1819, he wrote:

> I have read your Altham, & Keats' Poem & Lamb's Works - For the second in this list much praise is due to me for having read, the Author's intention appearing to be that no person should possibly get to the end of it. Yet it is full of some of the highest & the finest gleams of poetry; indeed everything seems to be viewed by the mind of a poet described in it. I think if he had printed about 50 pages of fragments from it I should have been led to admire Keats as a poet more than I ought, of which there is now no danger.'

Writing to Keats from Pisa on 27 July 1820, Shelley slightly revised his opinion of the poem:

> I have lately read your Endymion again & ever with a new sense of the treasures of poetry it contains, though treasures poured forth with indistinct profusion . . . In poetry *I* have sought to avoid system and mannerism; I wish those who excel me in genius, would pursue the same plan. -

'I am glad you take pleasure in my poor Poem,' Keats replied on 16 August, 'which I would willingly take the trouble to unwrite, if possible, did I care so much as I have done about Reputation.'

168*
John Keats
Lamia, Isabella, The Eve of St. Agnes, and Other Poems
1820
THE WORDSWORTH TRUST [THE BRITISH LIBRARY BOARD]

A copy of this great collection arrived in Italy on 11 October 1820. Its impact upon Shelley was profound, and he found in Keats new powers as a poet.

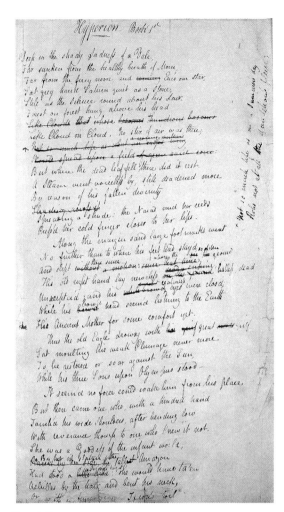

Cat. 169

169*
John Keats
Hyperion
September 1817 - April 1818
THE BRITISH LIBRARY BOARD

Of all Keats's poems, Shelley held *Hyperion* in particular regard. A fragment, it begins the story of Hyperion, the last of the Titans, and his eventual dethronement by Apollo. 'Keats' new volume has arrived to us,' he wrote to Marianne Hunt (see below), '& the fragment called Hyperion promises for him that he is destined to become one of the first writers of the age.' Again, in his preface to Adonais, Shelley writes:

> It is my intention to subjoin to the London edition of this poem, a criticism upon the claims of its lamented object to be classed among the highest genius who have adorned our age....I consider the fragment of *Hyperion*, as second to nothing that was ever produced by a writer of the same years.'

Keats himself, however, soon grew dissatisfied with the poem. 'I have given up Hyperion', he wrote to J.H. Reynolds in September 1819, 'there were too many Miltonic inversions in it - Miltonic verse cannot be written but in an artist's or rather artist's humour. I wish to give myself up to other sensations.

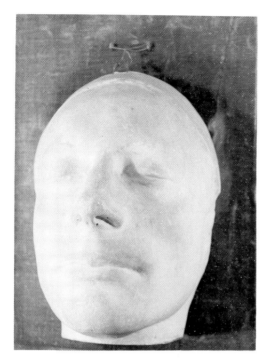

Cat. 170

170*
Lifemask of John Keats
By Benjamin Robert Haydon
H 22 cms
DALLAS PRATT COLLECTION

This lifemask was given to Robert Louis Stevenson by Shelley's surviving son, Percy Florence, during the year of Stevenson's residence at Bournemouth. Sir Percy saw in Stevenson's character an imagined resemblance to his father, and seems to have showered him with gifts, including a portrait of Shelley, a jewelled revolver, and a head-rest. Stevenson wrote to W.H. Lowe in 1886: `I have a look of him the poet Shelley, all of his sisters have noses like mine; Sir Percy's has a marked hook; all the family had high cheek-bones like mine.' He kept the lifemask with him in his study at Samoa.

Keats's sister Fanny told Harry Buxton Forman that the mask was 'a perfect copy of the features of my dear brother . . . except for the mouth . . . which renders the expression more severe than the sweet and mild original.'

171
Deathmask of John Keats
By Gheradi
H 28 cms
ETON SCHOOL

The original death mask was made by Gheradi on 24 February 1821, and white plaster casts were made by Charles Smith between 1886 and 1891. It is believed that this is one of three surviving casts.

172*
Percy Bysshe Shelley
Letter to Marianne Hunt
Bagni di Pisa, 29 October 1820
THE BRITISH LIBRARY BOARD

Shelley, who had just received a copy of Keats's *Lamia, Isabella, The Eve of St. Agnes, and Other Poems* (1820), singles out *Hyperion* for praise:

My dear Marianne
    I am delighted to hear that you complain of me for not writing to you, although I have much more reason to complain of you for not writing to me. At least it promises me a letter from you, and you know not with what pleasure we receive, & with what anxiety we expect intelligence from you - almost the only friends who now remain to us.-
    I am afraid that the strict system of expense to which you are limited, annoys you all very much, & that Hunts health suffers both from that, & from the incredible exertions which I see by the Indicators & the Examiners that he is making. Would to Heaven that I had the power of doing you some good - but when you are sure that the wish is sincere, the bare expression of it may help to cheer you.
    The Gisbornes are arrived, & have brought news of you, & some books; the principal part of which however are yet to arrive by sea. - Keats's new volume has arrived to us, & the fragment called Hyperion promises for him that he is destined to become one of the first writers of the age.- His other things are imperfect enough, & what is worse written in the bad sort of style which is becoming fashionable among those who fancy that they are imitating Hunt & Wordsworth. - But of all these things nothing is worse than a volume by Barry Cornwall entitled the Sicilian Story. The Sicilian story

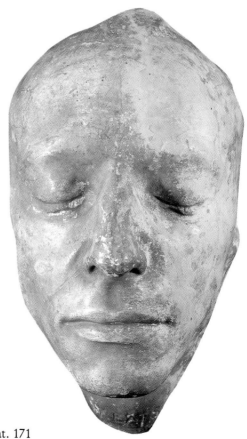

Cat. 171

itself is pretty enough, but the other things in the volume, I hope that Hunt thinks abominable, in spite of his extracting the only three good stanzas from Gyges with his usual good nature in the Examiner. Indeed I ought not to complain of Hunts good nature for no one owes so much to it. - Is not the vulgarity of these wretched imitations of Lord Byron carried to a pitch of the sublime? - His indecencies too both against sexual nature & against human nature in general sit very awkwardly upon him. He only affects the libertine; he is really a very aimiable friendly & agreable man I hear. But is not this monstrous? In Lord Byron all this has an analogy with the general system of his character, & the wit & poetry which surround, hide with their light the darkness of the thing itself. They contradict it even; they prove that the strength & beauty of human nature can survive & conquer all that appears most inconsistent with it. But for a writer to be at once filthy & dull - is a crime against gods men & columns. For heaven's sake do not shew this to any one but Hunt, for I would [not] irritate the wasps' nest of the irritable race of poets.

Where is Keats now? I am anxiously expecting him in Italy where I shall take care to bestow every possible attention on him. I consider his a most valuable life, & I am deeply interested in his safety. I intend to be the physician both of his body & his soul, to keep the one warm & to teach {the} other Greek & Spanish. I am aware indeed in part {tha}t I am nourishing a rival who will far surpass {me} and this is an additional motive & will be an added pleasure.

We are at this moment removing from the Bagni to Pisa, for the Serchio has broken its banks & all the country about us is under water. An old friend & fellow townsman of mine Captain Medwin is on a visit to us at present, & we anxiously expect Keats, to whom I would write if I knew where to address.

173*
Percy Bysshe Shelley
Letter to Claire Clairmont
Pisa, [16 June 1821]
THE BRITISH LIBRARY BOARD

Shelley sends Claire the news of Keats's recent death (he had died at Rome on 23 February), and reports that he has finished his elegy, *Adonais*:

> . . . Let me see if I have any news for you. I have received a most melancholy account of the last illness of poor Keats, which I will neither tell you nor send you; for it would make you too low-spirited. - My elegy on him is finished: I have dipped my pen in consuming fire to chastise his destroyers; otherwise the tone of the poem is solemn & exalted. - I send it to the press here, & you will soon have a copy.

174*
Percy Bysshe Shelley
Adonais
Pisa: with the types of Didot, 1821
PRIVATE COLLECTION [THE BRITISH LIBRARY BOARD]

The poem is at once grand in its scale, domestic in its feeling, satirical about literary politics, and visionary

ADONAIS

AN ELEGY ON THE DEATH OF JOHN KEATS, AUTHOR OF ENDYMION, HYPERION ETC.

BY

PERCY. B. SHELLEY

Ἀστὴρ πρίν μὲν ἔλαμπες ἐνι ζωοῖσιν ἑῶος.
Νῦν δὲ θανών, λάμπεις ἕσπερος ἐν φθιμένοις.
PLATO.

PISA

WITH THE TYPES OF DIDOT

MDCCCXXI.

in its positive attitude to Keats's death. Its conclusions are not complacent - there is a sense of hazard - the poet is both metaphysically and literally at sea while Keats is steadfast as a distant star.

This is the first edition of the poem, published with the types of Didot (a family of famous Parisian printers and type designers). 'The poem is beautifully printed', Shelley wrote to his English publisher Charles Ollier in July 1821, '& what is of more consequence, correctly: indeed it was to obtain this last point that I sent it to the press at Pisa.' In June he had sent to Ollier proof sheets, also with the types of Didot, of Taafe's translation of Dante's *Divine Comedy*. 'Pray observe the great beauty of the typography', he wrote, 'they are the same types as my elegy on Keats is printed from.'

The printer has been identified as Niccolo Capurrò, who in 1818 had published an Italian translation of Byron's *Lament of Tasso*, also with the types of Didot.

175*
Percy Bysshe Shelley
Adonais
THE WORDSWORTH TRUST

A transcription made in June 1828 by Wordsworth's daughter Dora for her future husband, Edward Quillinan, an acquaintance of Thomas Medwin.

Adonais

Here pause: these graves are all too young as yet
To have outgrown the sorrow which consigned
Its charge to each; and if the seal is set,
Here, on one fountain of a mourning mind,
Break it not thou! too surely shalt thou find
Thine own well full, if thou returnest home,
Of tears and gall. From the world's bitter wind
Seek shelter in the shadow of the tomb.
What Adonais is, why fear we to become?

The One remains, the many change and pass;
Heaven's light forever shines, Earth's shadows fly;
Life, like a dome of many-coloured glass,
Stains the white radiance of Eternity,
Until Death tramples it to fragments. - Die,
If thou wouldst be with that which thou dost seek!
Follow where all is fled! - Rome's azure sky,
Flowers, ruins, statues, music, words, are weak
The glory they transfuse with fitting truth to speak.

Why linger, why turn back, why shrink, my Heart?
Thy hopes are gone before: from all things here
They have departed; thou shouldst now depart!
A light is passed from the revolving year,
And man, and woman; and what still is dear
Attracts to crush, repels to make thee wither.
The soft sky smiles, - the low wind whispers near:
'Tis Adonais calls! oh, hasten thither,
No more let Life divide what Death can join together.

That Light whose smile kindles the Universe,
That Beauty in which all things work and move,
That Benediction which the eclipsing Curse
Of birth can quench not, that sustaining Love
Which through the web of being blindly wove
By man and beast and earth and air and sea,
Burns bright or dim, as each are mirrors of
The fire for which all thirst; now beams on me,
Consuming the last clouds of cold mortality.

The breath whose might I have invoked in song
Descends on me; my spirit's bark is driven,
Far from the shore, far from the trembling throng
Whose sails were never to the tempest given;
The massy earth and spherèd skies are riven!
I am borne darkly, fearfully, afar;
Whilst, burning through the inmost veil of Heaven,
The soul of Adonais, like a star,
Beacons from the abode where the Eternal are.

(Stanzas 51-55)

176*
Percy Bysshe Shelley
Elegy on the Death of Adonis
THE BRITISH LIBRARY BOARD

A translation by Shelley from the Greek of Bion, and
clearly a source for *Adonais*. Bion's theme is more
erotic than that of Shelley. Bion deals with the
relation between two lovers Venus and Adonis,
whereas Shelley shows Keats in relation to a mother
figure, Urania and Adonais. This is Shelley's version
of Bion:

> 'I mourn Adonis dead - loveliest Adonis -
> Dead, dead Adonis - and the Loves lament.
> Sleep no more, Venus, wrapped in purple woof -
> Wake, violet-stolèd queen, and weave the crown
> Of Death, - 'tis Misery calls, - for he is dead.
> The lovely one lies wounded in the mountains,
> His white thigh struck with the white tooth; he scarce
> Yet breathes; and Venus hangs in agony there.
> The dark blood wanders o'er his snowy limbs,
> His eyes beneath their lids are lustreless,
> The rose has fled from his wan lips, and there
> That kiss is dead, which Venus gathers yet . . .'

177
Joseph Severn (1793-1879)
Portrait by John Partridge
1825
Pencil 25.4 x 17.8 cms
NATIONAL PORTRAIT GALLERY, LONDON

Joseph Severn looked after Keats during his last
illness in Rome. 'a young artist of the highest promise', writes Shelley in his preface to *Adonais*, 'who, I
have been informed, "almost risked his own life, and
sacrificed every prospect to unwearied attendance
upon his dying friend. . . . may the unextinguished
Spirit of his illustrious friend animate the creations of
his pencil, and plead against Oblivion for his name!'
Severn's posthumous, idealised portrait of Shelley
depicts him composing *Prometheus Unbound* at the
Baths of Caracalla.

Death

On 8 July 1822 Shelley set sail for Lerici with Edward Williams and their English boat boy, Charles Vivien. A sudden storm blew up, and Shelley's boat, the *Don Juan*, went down. Eight days later the bodies of Shelley, Williams and Vivien were found washed ashore.

To some critics, Shelley's early and sudden death is a kind of suicide; they take his need to pursue, and his sense of being pursued, as obsessive. In his poem *Adonais* he appears to express a death wish, for the poet seems ready to leave his present life and to bind himself to the steadfastness of the shining star of the now dead Keats:

> Why linger, why turn back, why shrink my Heart?
> Thy hopes are gone before; from all things here
> They have departed; thou shouldst now depart.

But the idea that Shelley was in some way in love with death forgets that poetry inevitably deals with what Keats called 'the knowledge of contrast, feeling for light and shade, all that information (primitive sense) necessary for a poem'. Shelley's ability to find vision and illumination necessarily involved a probing into the darker aspects of the human mind. Descriptions of Shelley as he was before fatally setting sail from Livorno on the Gulf of Spezia, to his home at Casa Magni, where his family and chosen friends were living, suggest his mood was one of delight, and that his mind was filled with future projects. Shelley died at the height of his powers - that very moment he had achieved perhaps his finest technical achievement in verse, his use of the metre of Dante in *The Triumph of Life*. He appears, from his last poems, to have been falling in love with Jane Williams, and these pieces are celebrations. At the same time, as Shelley's idealism matured, so it became coloured by a profound stoicism. Nine days before his death he wrote to Horace Smith, recalling the restless political activity of his earlier days in England:

> It seems to me that things have now arrived at such a crisis as requires every man plainly to utter his sentiments on the inefficacy of the existing religions no less than political systems for restraining & guiding mankind. Let us see the truth whatever that may be. - The destiny of man can scarcely be so degraded that he was born only to die: and if such should be the case, delusions, especially the gross & preposterous ones of the existing religion, can scarcely be supposed to exalt it. - if every man said what he thought, it could not subsist a day. But all, more or less, subdue themselves to the element that surrounds them, & contribute to the evils they lament by the hypocrisy that springs from them. - England appears to be in a desperate condition, Ireland still worse, & no class of those who subsist on the public labour will be persuaded that *their* claims on it must be diminished. But the government must content itself with less in taxes, the landholder must submit to receive less rent, & the fundholder a diminished interest, - or they will all get nothing, or something worse {than} nothing. - I once thought to study these affairs & write or act in them - I am glad that my good genius said *refrain*. I see little public virtue, & I foresee that the contest will be one of blood & gold two elements, which however much to my taste in my pockets & my veins, I have an objection to out of them.

There was much writing to come about Shelley. But one great work came from Mary Shelley, and that was her letter to Maria Gisborne, one of the finest of English letters, where she describes the events immediately before and after Shelley's death. It is a letter that is at once confessional and matter of fact; so we hear of Mary's own depression which derived from her miscarriage, of daytime visions and strange nightmares, of Mary's and Jane's desperate journey to find out what had happened to their husbands, and of the final discoveries and sad obsequies. All the three women in the household - Mary, Claire, Jane - have to show courage. Mary is at once eloquent and adequate to her theme.

Cat. 183

178*
Percy Bysshe Shelley
Letter to Jane Williams
Pisa, 4 July 1822

This is the last surviving letter Shelley wrote, composed only four days days before he set sail for Lerici with Edward Williams. He seems to have expected Williams to go on ahead of him, but in the event Williams stayed behind because, as he wrote to Jane, 'I know [Shelley] secretly wishes me not to leave him in the lurch.' Jane Williams answered Shelley's letter on 6 July, adding a postscript: 'Why do you talk of never enjoying moments like the past, are you going to join your friend Plato or do you expect I shall do so soon?'

> You will probably see Williams before I can disentangle myself from the affairs with which I am now surrounded - I return to Leghorn tonight & shall urge him to sail with the first fair wind without expecting me. I have thus the pleasure of contributing to your happiness when deprived of every other - and of leaving you no other subject of regret, but the absence of one scarcely worth regretting. - I fear you are solitary & melancholy at Villa Magni - & in the intervals of the greater & more serious distress in which I am compelled to sympathize here, I figure to myself the countenance which has been the source of such consolation to me, shadowed by a veil of sorrow
>
> How soon those hours past, & how slowly they return to pass so soon again, & perhaps for ever, in which we have lived together so intimately so happily! - Adieu, my dearest friend - I only write these lines for the pleasure of tracing what will meet your eyes. - Mary will tell you all the news.
> S.

180
Frederick Leighton (1830-1869)
Steps in Lerici
Oil on Canvas 17 x 9.3 cms

The Shelley's move to Lerici, a fishing village in the bay of Spezia, in April 1822 coincided with the death of Allegra at the convent of Bagnacavallo. 'Nature is here as vivid and joyous as we are dismal,' Shelley wrote to Byron on 3 May, 'and we have built, as Faust says, "our little world in the great world of all" as a contrast rather than a copy of that divine example.' They stayed at the Villa Magni, a former boathouse lying right by the shore, which Mary Shelley later described in such detail in a letter to Maria Gisborne (entry no. 188).

The Villa Magni, Lerici

Cat. 181

181*
Edward Ellerker Williams
Sketches of the *Don Juan* and the *Bolivar*
*c.*1822
Photograph 42 x 37 cms
THE WORDSWORTH TRUST

The Don Juan (top), was Shelley's boat at Lerici. He and Byron had planned to spend much of the summer sailing, and so commissioned a Captain Daniel Roberts, RN, to build a boat for each poet at Genoa. Shelley reported the arrival of the *Don Juan*, a twenty-four-foot yacht to Captain Roberts on 13 May 1822:

The Don Juan arrived safe on the evening of Sunday [12 May] after a long and stormy passage . . . She is a most beautiful boat, & so far surpasses both mine & Williams's expectations that it was with some difficulty that we could pesuade ourselves that you had not sent us the Bolivar by mistake.

The *Bolivar* (bottom) was Byron's much larger boat, which arrived at Lerici on 13 June.

The name of Don Juan was Trelawny's idea, and it was Shelley's intention to paint it out and replace it with the name *Ariel*, but the boat which Shelley and Edward Williams and the ship's-boy Charles Vivien went down on the afternoon of 8th July 1822 was still the *Don Juan*.

Cat. 140 Julia Margaret Cameron, *Beatrice Cenci*

Cat. 68 Mary Shelley by Richard Rothwell

182*
Some of the poet's ashes with fragments of his skull
THE BRITISH LIBRARY BOARD

The bodies of Shelley, Williams, and their sailor boy were found washed ashore between 16-18 July. Under the direction of Trelawny, and in the presence of Leigh Hunt and Byron, their bodies were exhumed from their shallow graves in the sand and cremated on the shore.

183*
Louis-Eduard Fournier
Shelley's Funeral Rites
Photograph
THE WORDSWORTH TRUST

A photograph of an original painting in the Walker Art Gallery, Liverpool. The figures watching Shelley's funeral pyre are, from the left, Trelawny, Leigh Hunt and Byron. In later life, Trelawny would show visitors the scar he had gained when plucking out Shelley's heart from the ashes.

Cat. 184

184*
William Bright Morris (1834-1900)
Keats' Grave and the Pyramid of Cestius, Testaccio Cemetary, Rome - 1817
1870
Pastel 17 x 25 cms
PRIVATE COLLECTION

Shelley's ashes were buried alongside the grave of John Keats, and near to the grave of his son William, in the Protestant cemetery, Rome.

185*
Thomas Hardy
Rome. At the Pyramid of Cestius near the Graves of Shelley and Keats
1887
THE BRITISH LIBRARY BOARD

Thomas Hardy saw the graves of Keats and Shelley when visiting Rome with his wife in 1887. Hardy

Cat. 185

admired Shelley more than any other poet, and there are many echoes of 'our most marvellous lyrist' in his prose as well as his poetry. In *Tess of the D'Urbervilles* Angel Clare is described as being 'less Byronic than Shelleyan'.

> Who, then, was Cestius,
> And what is he to me? -
> Amid thick thoughts and memories multitudinous
> One thought alone brings he.
>
> I can recall no word
> Of anything he did;
> For me he is a man who died and was interred
> To leave a pyramid
>
> Whose purpose was exprest
> Not with its first design,
> Nor till, far down in Time, beside it found their rest
> Two countrymen of mine.
>
> Cestius in life, maybe,
> Slew, breathed out threatening;
> I know not. This I know: in death all silently
> He does a finer thing,
>
> In beckoning pilgrim feet
> With marble finger high
> To where, by shadowy wall and history-haunted street,
> Those matchless singers lie . . .
>
> Say, then, he lived and died
> That stones which bear his name
> Should mark, through Time, where two immortal Shades abide;
> It is an ample fame.'

186*
Mary Shelley
The Choice
1822
THE BRITISH LIBRARY BOARD

A poem by Mary Shelley, composed on her husband's death:

Ah! he is gone - and I alone;
　　How dark and dreary seems the time!
'Tis thus when the glad sun is flown,
　　Night rushes o'er the Indian clime.

Is there no star to cheer this night -
　　No soothing twilight for the breast?
Yes - Memory sheds her fairy light,
　　Beaming at sunset's golden west.

And hope of dawn - Oh brighter far
　　Than clouds that in the Orient burn,
More welcome than the morning star,
　　Is the dear thought - he will return!

187*
Mary Shelley
Letter to Lord Byron
22 Ocotber 1822
<small>JOHN MURRAY COLLECTION</small>

Mary Shelley here describes how her father William Godwin received the news of Shelley's death 'without any expression or outward sign of sorrow'. The reporter, quoted by Mary, is Maria Gisborne, a warm friend to both the Shelleys; Maria goes on to state that when she met Peacock 'a tear did force itself into my eye'. Mary then turns to discuss Allegra's burial place at Harrow.

My dear Lord Byron
　　The letters that I received today were from Jane, Claire & Mrs Gisborne, nothing about *business* in any of them; indeed I do not expect to hear from my father before the expiration of a week. Mrs. Gisborne saw him; she says "I saw him alone, we spoke of you & of the ever to be lamented catastrophe without any expression or outward sign of sorrow. I thought that he had erred in his memorable assertion & that we human beings really were stocks & stones. When Peacock called upon me a tear did force itself into my eye in spite of all my struggles."

　　But I do not write to your Lordship to tell you this, but to mention another subject in her letter. She says "When Mr. Gisborne went to Harrow, to accompany a son of Mr. Clementis' who is placed in the Harrow school, he saw the grave of poor Allegra. This was precisely the day your father called on me, the funeral had taken place the day preceding. There was a great outcry among the ultra purists on the occasion, and at the time they seemed resolved that the inscription intended by her father, should not be placed in the church. These Gentlemen would willingly cast an eternal veil over King David's infirmities & their own, but the world will peep through, even though poor Allegra should be without the honours of her inscription." . . . I have nearly finished copying your *savage* Canto You will cause Milman to hang himself "non c'é altro rimedio" I was much pleased with your notice of Keats your fashionable world is delightful & your *dove* you mention eight years exactly the eight years that comprizes all my years of happiness Where also is he, who gone has made this quite, quite another earth from that which it was? There might be [have been] something sunny about me then, now I am truly *cold moonshine*.

In this last phrase Mary accepts the justice, for the sad present, of Shelley's cold characterisation of her as the white moon in Epispychidion.

Cat. 188

188*
Mary Shelley
Letter to Maria Gisborne
15 August 1822
<small>THE BRITISH LIBRARY BOARD</small>

Soon after Shelley's death, Mary Shelley recounts to her friend 'the last miserable months of my disastrous life'. Arguably one of the great letters in English, certainly a finer elegy than her poem, *The Choice*, and above all a letter marked with a matter-of-fact detail which comes from the eye of the novelist.

　　I said in a letter to Peacock, my dear Mrs. Gisborne, that I would send you some account of the last miserable months of my disastrous life. From day to day I have put this off, but I will now endeavour to fulfil my design. The scene of my existence is closed & though there be no pleasure in retracing the scenes that have preceded the event which has crushed my hopes yet there seems to be a necessity in doing so, and I obey the impulse that urges me. I wrote to you either at the end of May or the beginning of June. I described to you the place we were living in: - our desolate house, the beauty yet strangeness of the scenery and the delight Shelley took in all this - he never was in better health or spirits than during this time. I was not well in body or mind. My nerves were wound up to the utmost irritation, and the sense of misfortune hung over my spirits. No words can tell you how I hated our house & the country about it. Shelley reproached me for this - his health was good & the place was quite after his own heart - What could I answer - that the people were wild & hateful, that though the country was beautiful yet I liked a more *countrified* place, that there was great difficulty in living - that all our Tuscans would leave us, & that the very jargon of these *Genovese* was disgusting - This was all I had to say but no words could describe my feelings - the beauty of the woods made me weep & shudder - so vehement was my feeling of dislike that I used to rejoice when the winds & waves permitted me to go out in the boat so that I was not obliged to take my usual walk among tree shaded paths, allies of vine festooned trees - all that before I doated on & that now weighed on me. My only moments of peace were on board that unhappy boat, when lying down with my head on his knee I shut my eyes & felt the wind & our swift motion alone. My ill health might account for much of this - bathing in the sea somewhat relieved me - but on the 8th of June (I think it was) I was threatened with a miscarriage, & after a week of great ill health on sunday the 16th this took place at eight in the morning. I was so ill that for seven hours I lay nearly lifeless kept from fainting by brandy, vinegar eau de Cologne &c at length ice was brought to our solitude - it came before the doctor so Claire & Jane were afraid of using it but Shelley over[r]uled them & by an unsparing application of it I was restored. They all thought & so did I at one time that I was about to die I hardly wish that I had, my own Shelley could never have lived without me, the sense of eternal misfortune would have pressed to[o] heavily upon him, & what would have become of my poor babe? My convalescence was slow and during it a strange occurence happened to retard it. But first I must describe our house to you. The floor on which we lived was thus [Here there is a diagram of the floor plan] 1 is a terrace that went the whole length of our house & was precipitous to the sea. 2 the large dining hall - 3, a private staircase. 4, my bedroom, 5 Mrs. W[illiam]'s bedroom, 6 Shelley's & 7 the entrance from the great staircase. Now to return. As I said Shelley was at first in perfect health but having over fatigued himself one day, & then the fright my illness gave him caused a return of nervous sensations & visions as bad as in his worst times. I think it was the saturday after my illness [22nd] while yet unable to walk I was confined to my bed - in the middle of the night I was awoke by hearing him scream & come rushing into my room; I was sure that he was asleep & tried to waken him by calling on him, but he continued to scream which inspired me with such a panic that I jumped out of bed & ran across the hall to Mrs. W[illiam]'s room where I fell through weakness, though I was so frightened that I got up again immediately - she let me in & Williams went to S[helley] who had been wakened by my getting out of bed - he said that he had not been asleep & that it was a vision that he saw that had frightened him - But as he declared that he had not screamed it was certainly a dream & no waking vision - What had frightened him was this - He dreamt that lying as he did in bed Edward & Jane came in to him, they were in the most horrible condition, their bodies lacerated - their bones starting through their skin, the faces pale yet stained with blood, they could hardly walk, but Edward was the weakest & Jane was supporting him - Edward said - Get up, Shelley, the sea is flooding the house & it is all coming down." S[helley] got up, he thought, & went to the *[sic]* his window that looked on the terrace & the sea & thought he saw the sea rushing in. Suddenly his vision changed & he saw the figure of himself strangling me, that had made him rush into my room, yet fearful of frightening me he dared not approch [sic] the bed, when my jumping out awoke him, or as he phrased it caused his vision to vanish. All this was frightful enough, & talking it over the next morning he told me that he had had many visions lately - he had seen the figure of himself which met him as he walked on the terrace & said to him - "How long do you mean to be content" - no very terrific words & certainly not prophetic of what has

occurred. But Shelley had often seen these figures when ill; but the strangest thing is that Mrs. W[illiams] saw him. Now Jane though a woman of sensibility, has not much imagination & is not in the slightest degree nervous - neither in dreams or otherwise. She was standing one day, the day before I was taken ill, at a window that looked on the Terrace with Trelawny - it was day - she saw as she thought Shelley pass by the window, as he often was then, without a coat or jacket - he passed again - now as he passed both times the same way - and as from the side towards which he went each time there was no way to get back except past the window again (except over a wall twenty feet from the ground) she was struck at seeing him pass twice thus & looked out & seeing him no more she cried - "Good God can Shelley have leapt from the wall? Where can he be gone?" Shelley, said Trelawny - "no Shelley has past - What do you mean?" Trelawny says that she trembled exceedingly when she heard this & it proved indeed that Shelley had never been on the terrace & was far off at the time she saw him. Well we thought [no] more of these things & I slowly got better. Having heard from Hunt that he had sailed from Genoa, on Monday July 1st S[helley], Edward & Captain Roberts (the Gent. who built our boat) departed in our boat for Leghorn to receive him - I was then just better, had begun to crawl from my bedroom to the terrace; but bad spirits succe[e]ded to ill health, and this departure of Shelley's seemed to add insuf[f]erably to my misery. I could not endure that he should go - I called him back two or three times, & told him that if I did not see him soon I would go to Pisa with the child - I cried bitterly when he went away. They went & Jane, Claire & I remained alone with the children - I could not walk out, & though I gradually gathered strength it was slowly & my ill spirits encreased; in my letters to him I entreated him to return - "the feeling that some misfortune would happen," I said, "haunted me": I feared for the child, for the idea of danger connected with him never struck me - When Jane & Claire took their evening walk I used to patrole the terrace, oppressed with wretchedness, yet gazing on the most beautiful scene in the world. This Gulph of Spezia is subdivided into many small bays of which ours was far the most beautiful the two horns of the bay (so to express myself) were wood covered promontories crowned with castles - at the foot of these on the furthest was Lerici, on the nearest Sant Arenzo - Lerici being above a mile by land from us & San Arenzo about a hundred or two yards - trees covered the hills that enclosed this bay & then beautiful groups were picturesquely contrasted with the rocks the castle on [and] the town - the sea lay far extended in front while to the west we saw the promontory & islands which formed one of the extreme boundarys of the Gulph - to see the sun set upon this scene, the stars shine & the moon rise was a sight of wondrous beauty, but to me it added only to my wretchedness - I repeated to myself all that another would have said to console me, & told myself the tale of love peace & competence which I enjoyed - but I answered myself by tears - did not my William die? & did I hold my Percy by a firmer tenure? - Yet I thought when he, when my Shelley returns I shall be happy - he will comfort me, if my boy be ill he will restore him & encourage me. I had a letter or two from Shelley mentioning the difficulties he had in establishing the Hunts, & that he was unable to fix the time of his return. Thus a week past. On Monday 8th Jane had a letter from Edward, dated saturday, he said that he waited at Leghorn for S[helley] who was at Pisa.

That S[helley]'s return was certain, "but" he continued, "if he should not come by monday I will come in a felucca, & you may expect me teusday evening at furthest." This was monday, the fatal monday, but with us it was stormy all day & we did not at all suppose that they could put to sea. At twelve at night we had a thunderstorm; Teusday [9th] it rained all day & was calm - the sky wept on their graves - on Wednesday [10th] - the wind was fair from Leghorn & in the evening several felucca's arrived thence - one brought word that they had sailed Monday, but we did not believe them - thursday [11th] was another day of fair wind & when twelve at night came & we did not see the tall sails of the little boat double the promontory before us we began to fear not the truth, but some illness - some disagreable news for their detention. Jane got so uneasy that she determined to proceed the next day to Leghorn in a boat to see what was the matter - friday [12th] came & with it a heavy sea & bad wind - Jane however resolved to be rowed to Leghorn (since no boat could sail) and busied herself in preparations - I wished her to wait for letters, since friday was letter day - she would not - but the sea detained her, the swell rose so that no boat would venture out - At 12 at noon our letters came - there was one from Hunt to Shelley, it said - "pray write to tell us how you got home, for they say that you had bad weather after you sailed monday & we are anxious" - the paper fell from me - I trembled all over - Jane read it - "Then it is all over!" she said. "No, my dear Jane," I cried, "it is not all over, but this suspense is dreadful - come with me, we will go to Leghorn, we will post to be swift & learn our fate." We crossed to Lerici, despair in our hearts; they raised our spirits there by telling us that no accident had been heard of & that it must have been known &c - but still our fear was great - & without resting we posted to Pisa. It must have been fearful to see us - two poor, wild, aghast creatures driving - (like Matilda) towards the *sea* to learn if we were to be for ever doomed to misery. I knew that Hunt was at Pisa at Lord Byron's house but I thought that L[ord] B[yron] was at Leghorn. I settled that we should drive to Casa Lanfranchi that I should get out & ask the fearful question of Hunt, "Do you know any thing of Shelley?" On entering Pisa the idea of seeing Hunt for the first time for four years under such circumstances, & asking him such a question was so terrific to me that it was with difficulty that I prevented myself from going into convulsions - my struggles were dreadful - they knocked at the door & some one called out "Che é?" it was the Guiccioli's maid. L[ord] B[yron] was in Pisa - Hunt was in bed, so I was to see LB. instead of him. This was a great relief to me; I staggered up stairs - the Guiccioli came to meet me smiling while I could hardly say - "Where is he - Sapete alcuna cosa di Shelley" - They knew nothing - he had left Pisa on sunday - on Monday he had sailed - there had been bad weather Monday afternoon - more they knew not. Both L[ord] B[yron] & the lady have told me since - that on that terrific evening I looked more like a ghost than a woman - light seemed to emanate from my features, my face was very white, I looked like marble - Alas, I had risen almost from a bed of sickness for this journey - I had travelled all day - it was now 12 at night - & we, refusing to rest, proceeded to Leghorn - not in despair - no, for then we must have died; but with sufficient hope to keep up the agitation of the spirits which was all my life. It was past two in the morning [13th] when we arrived - They took us to the wrong inn - neither Trelawny or Capn Roberts were there nor did we exactly know where they were

so we were obliged to wait until daylight. We threw ourselves drest on our beds & slept a little but at 6 o'clock we went to one or two inns to ask for one or the other of these gentlemen. We found Roberts at the Globe. He came down to us with a face which seemed to tell us that the worst was true, and here we learned all that occurred during the week they had been absent from us, & under what circumstances they had departed on their return. Shelley had past most of the time a[t] Pisa - arranging the affairs of the Hunts & skrewing L[ord] B[yron]'s mind to the sticking place about the journal. He had found this a difficult task at first but at length he had succeeded to his heart's content with both points. Mrs. Mason said that she saw him in better health and spirits than she had ever known him, when he took leave of her sunday July 7th His face burnt by the sun, & his heart light that he had succeeded in rendering the Hunts' tolerably comfortable. Edward had remained at Leghorn. On Monday July 8th during the morning they were employed in buying many things - eatables &c for our solitude. There had been a thunderstorm early but about noon the weather was fine & the wind right fair for Lerici - They were impatient to be gone. Roberts said, "Stay until tomorrow to see if the weather is settled; & S[helley] might have staid but Edward was in so great an anxiety to reach home - saying they would get there in seven hours with that wind - that they sailed! S[helley] being in one of those extravagant fits of good spirits in which you have sometimes seen him. Roberts went out to the end of the mole & watched them out of sight - they sailed at one & went off at the rate of about 7 knots - About three - Roberts, who was still on the mole - saw wind coming from the Gulph - or rather what the Italians call a temporale - anxious to know how the boat w[oul]d weather the storm, he got leave to go up the tower & with the glass discovered them about ten miles out at sea, off Via Reggio, they were taking in their topsails - "The haze of the storm," he said, "hid them from me & I saw them no more - when the storm cleared I looked again fancying that I should see them on their return to us - but there was no boat on the sea." - This then was all we knew, yet we did not despair - they might have been driven over to Corsica & not knowing the coast & [have] Gone god knows where. Reports favoured this belief - it was even said that they had been seen in the Gulph - We resolved to return with all possible speed - We sent a courier to go from tower to tower along the coast to know if any thing had been seen or found, & at 9 A.M. we quitted Leghorn - stopped but one moment at Pisa & proceeded towards Lerici When at 2 miles from Via Reggio we rode down to that town to know if they knew any thing - here our calamity first began to break on us - a little boat & a water cask had been found five miles off - they had manufactured a *piccolissima lancia* of thin planks stitched by a shoemaker just to let them run on shore without wetting themselves as our boat drew 4 feet [of] water. - the description of that found tallied with this - but then this boat was very cumbersome & in bad weather they might have been easily led to throw it overboard - the cask frightened me most - but the same reason might in some sort be given for that. I must tell you that Jane & I were not now alone - Trelawny accompanied us back to our home. We journied on & reached the Magra about 1/2 past ten P.M. I cannot describe to you what I felt in the first moment when, fording this river, I felt the water splash about our wheels - I was suffocated - I gasped for breath - I thought I should have gone into convulsions, & I struggled violently that Jane might not perceive it - looking down the river I saw the two great lights burning at the *foce* - A voice from within me seemed to cry aloud that is his grave. After passing the river I gradually recovered. Arriving at Lerici we [were] obliged to cross our little bay in a boat - San Arenzo was illuminated for a festa - What a scene - the roaring sea - the scirocco wind - the lights of the town towards which we rowed - & our own desolate hearts - that coloured all with a shroud - We landed; nothing had been heard of them. This was saturday July 13. & thus we waited until Thursday July 25 [*error for* 18] thrown about by hope & fear. We sent messengers along the coast towards Genoa & to Via Reggio - nothing had been found more than the *lancetta;* reports were brought us - we hoped - & yet to tell you all the agony we endured during those 12 days would be to make you conceive a universe of pain - each moment intolerable & giving place to one still worse. The people of the country too added to one's discomfort - they are like wild savages - on festas' the men & women & children in different bands - the sexes always separate - pass the whole night in dancing on the sands close to our door running into the sea then back again & screaming all the time one perpetuel air - the most detestable in the world - then the scirocco perpetually blew & the sea for ever moaned their dirge. On thursday 25th [*should be* 18th] Trelawny left us to go to Leghorn to see what was doing or what could be done. On friday [19th] I was very ill but as evening came on I said to Jane - "If any thing had been found on the coast Trelawny would have returned to let us know. He has not returned so I hope."

About 7 oclock P.M. he did return - all was over - all was quiet now, they had been found washed on shore - Well all this was to be endured.

Well what more have I to say ? The next day [20th] we returned to Pisa And here we are still Days pass away - one after another - & we live thus. We are all together - we shall quit Italy together. Jane must proceed to London - if letters do not alter my views I shall remain in Paris. - Thus we live - Seeing the Hunts now & then. Poor Hunt has suffered terribly as you may guess. Lord Byron is very kind to me & comes with the Guiccioli to see me often.

Today - this day - the sun shining in the sky - they are gone to the desolate sea coast to perform the last offices to their earthly remains. Hunt, L[ord] B[yron] & Trelawny. The quarantine laws would not permit us to remove them sooner - & now only on condition that we burn them to ashes. That I do not dislike - His rest shall be at Rome beside my child - where one day I also shall join them - Adonais is not Keats's it is his own elegy - he bids you there go to Rome. - I have seen the spot where he now lies - the sticks that mark the spot where the sands cover him - he shall not be [burned] there it is too nea[r] Via Reggio - They are now about this fearful office - & I live!

One more circumstance I will mention. As I said he took leave of Mrs. Mason in high spirits on sunday - "Never," said she, "did I see him look happier than the last glance I had of his countenance." On Monday he was lost - on Monday night she dreamt that she was somewhere - she knew not where & he came looking very pale & fearfully melancholy - she said to him - "You look ill, you are tired, sit down & eat." "No," he replied, "I shall never eat more; I have not a *soldo* left in the world." - "Nonsense," said she, "this is no inn - you need not pay" - "Perhaps, he answered, "it is the worse for that." Then she awoke & going to sleep again she dreamt that my Percy was dead & she awoke

crying bitterly - so bitterly & felt so miserable - that she said to herself - "Why if the little boy should die I should not feel it in this manner." She wa[s] so struck with these dreams that she mentioned them to her servant the next day - saying she hoped all was well with us.

Well here is my story - the last story I shall have to tell - all that might have been bright in my life is now despoiled - I shall live to improve myself, to take care of my child, & render myself worthy to join him. Soon my weary pilgrimage will begin - I rest now - but soon I must leave Italy - & then - there is an end of all but despair. Adieu I hope you are well & happy. I have an idea that while he was at Pisa that he received a letter from you that I have never seen - so not knowing where to direct I shall send this letter to Peacock - I shall send it open - he may be glad to read it -
Your's ever truly
Mary W S.

[P.S.] I shall probably write to you soon again. I have left out a material circumstance - A Fishing boat saw them go down - It was abou[t] 4 in the afternoon - they saw the boy at mast head, when baffling winds struck the sails they had looked away a moment & looking again the boat was gone - This is thei[r] story but there is little down [doubt] that these men might have saved them, at least Edward who could swim. They c[oul]d not they said get near her - but 3 quarters of an hour after passed over the spot where they had seen her - they protested no wreck of her was visible, but Roberts going on board their boat found several spars belonging to her - perhaps they let them perish to obtain these Trelawny thinks he can get her up, since another fisherman things [thinks] that he has found the spot where she lies, having drifted near shore. T[relawny] does this to know perhaps the cause of her wreck - but I care little about it.

An Ineffectual Angel?

After Shelley's death Mary was forbidden by Shelley's father, Sir Timothy, to write a memoir. Nevertheless the poems made their way. *Posthumous Poems*, 1824, and even more the edition of 1839 provided the public with their texts. Mary's notes provide an insight into the nature of the writer and the particular circumstances in which the poems were written. Her work is a brilliant act of presentation, and nothing brings out better how Shelley's best work came out of their lives together, full of turmoil and unhappiness though it often was. Appetite for information grew. Thomas Medwin, Shelley's cousin, published a *Memoir* in 1833 and a *Life* in 1847. These in turn stimulated the family to commission Thomas Jefferson Hogg to write an authorised life. This was a disappointment to Jane, the wife of Shelley's son, Sir Percy Florence Shelley, and in 1859 she put forward her own *Shelleyan Memorials: From Authentic Sources*. Jane's tendency to hagiography was to make the later revelations about Shelley, and particularly his relations with Harriet, their separation and her suicide, seem all the more shocking. Edward Dowden's candid biography in 1886 inspired Matthew Arnold's dismissal: 'What a set!'

Arnold's moralising over Shelley as the 'ineffectual angel', in itself such a brilliant satiric flight of judgement, is in part answered by Stopford Brooke's more optimistic assessment of the state of culture and progressive ideas. Even Arnold's negative comment is based upon an essay by Joubert on Plato. Plato, he notes, 'teaches us nothing; but he prepares us, fashions us, and makes us ready to know all. . . . Plato loses himself in the void, but one sees the play of his wings, one hears their rustle. . . . It is good to breathe his air but not to live upon him'. Nothing could be more fitting than that Shelley should be put in the context of Plato - if one has reservations about Plato, one might also have reservations about Shelley.

Shelley's younger contemporaries, such as John Stuart Mill or Henry Taylor, were soon reading him, as was Wordsworth's daughter Dora, who copied out *Adonais* in her own handwriting. Certainly her father knew Shelley's work and told his nephew, Christopher, that 'Shelley is one of the best *artists* of us all: I mean in workmanship of style.' Although Wordsworth didn't care for Shelley's opposition to all established things, or for his failure, in 'To a Skylark', despite the poem being full of imagination, to show 'the same observation of nature as his [Wordsworth's] own poem on the same bird did.' Wordsworth recognised that Shelley was a contender for the highest accolade: he told Gladstone: 'Shelley had the greatest native powers in poetry of all men of his age'. Browning in his early life saw this, and used Shelley as his master when he came to write his most original volume of poetry: *Men and Women*. In depicting these Renaissance figures Browning must be reading *The Cenci* more than *Prometheus Unbound*. What makes this poet live is his capacity to present us with the process of thinking through verse on all subjects under the sun.

Cat. 189

189*
Matthew Arnold (1822-1888)
*c.*1860
Photograph 27.5 x 21 cms
THE WORDSWORTH TRUST

One of the earliest photographs of Matthew Arnold, taken when he was Professor of Poetry at Oxford University.

190
Lord Byron
Poetry of Byron Chosen and Arranged by Matthew Arnold
London: Macmillan and Co., 1881
THE WORDSWORTH TRUST

In one of the most memorable judgements of the Romantic movement, Arnold's rhetoric in his preface to this selection manages to elevate Wordsworth and Byron above Keats, Coleridge and Shelley. An unwillingness to accept Arnold's judgement against Shelley is demonstrated by Stopford Brooke's address to the Shelley Society (entry no. 204), which responds to Shelley's power to illuminate notions of progress, and the betterment of human life.

> Wordsworth and Byron stand, it seems to me, first and pre-eminent in actual performance, a glorious pair among the English poets of this century. Keats had probably, indeed, a more consummate poetic gift than either of them; but he died having produced too little and being as yet too immature to rival them. I for my part can never even think of equalling with them any other of their contemporaries; - either Coleridge, poet

and philosopher wrecked in a mist of opium; or Shelley, beautiful and ineffectual angel, beating in the void his luminous wings in vain. Wordsworth and Byron stand out by themselves.

191
Mary Shelley (1797-1851)
Letter to Leigh Hunt
London, 28 December 1825
THE BRITISH LIBRARY BOARD

Mary Shelley writes to Hunt three years after Shelley's death. Already there is a concern that the more questionable incidents of the poet's life, particularly with regard to his first wife, are recorded carefully.

Mary Shelley described Harriet, shortly after her return from the Continent in September 1814, as 'certainly a very odd creature'.

> My dear Hunt
>   You may remember that immediately on reading your Mss [manuscript] concerning our Shelley, I wrote to you thanking you for it and pointing out a few mistakes or omissions to be rectified or made, and I sent it back to Mr. Bowring with my approval. I could not therefore have spoken of it in the terms quoted as mine. - I afterwards found that Peacock had it & he mentioned to me a circumstance which I wondered had not struck me before - but which is vital. It regards Shelley & Harriet - where you found your reasoning on a mistake as to fact - they did not part by mutual consent - and Shelley's justification, to me obvious, rests on other grounds; so that you would be obliged to remodel a good part of your writing. Peacock was urgent that such a mistake should not pass, and on account of various arrangements with Sir T[imothy] S[helley] was unwilling that it should be printed. I should have wrote concerning this to you, but your speedy arrival was announced - and I delayed mentioning it till I saw you. - I have not seen Mr. Bowring or communicated with him on the subject since the note mentioned above. Peacock is in possession of the Mss.
> I am, My dear Hunt
> Yours affectionately
> Mary Shelley

192
Thomas Jefferson Hogg
Shelley at Oxford
London: Methuen & Co., 1904
THE WORDSWORTH TRUST

Thomas Jefferson Hogg was chosen as the first official biographer of Shelley, and as such was in no position to be objective. The picture it gives us of Shelley is also limited, however, by Hogg's reluctance to talk about the poet rather than himself. Written with considerable comic zest, both this, and his subsequent, unfinished *Life of Shelley*, are nevertheless careless about the detailed nuances of Shelley's character.

193
Edward John Trelawny
Records of Shelley, Byron, and the Author
London: Basil Montague, 1878
THE WORDSWORTH TRUST

Trelawny's recollections are concerened less with facts than with the creation of myth, but, less egotistical than Hogg, the impression he gives of both Shelley and Byron often rings true. The title is revealing; Trelawny's concern was not just with the poets themselves, but also with the quite different effects they had upon upon his own life.

In later years he tried to woo Claire Clairmont. While she recognised him as honourable and worthy, she was unable to give herself to any man after the intensity of her quite different relationships with both Shelley and Byron.

194
Thomas Medwin
Memoir of Percy Bysshe Shelley
London: Whittaker, Treacher, & Co., 1833
THE WORDSWORTH TRUST

Thomas Medwin was a cousin of Shelley on his mother's side of the family, and this family connection gave him a special knowledge of the poet as a boy, since they were at school together at Syon House. Like Trelawny and Hogg, he will often forsake accuracy in order to create a particular impression.

195
Thomas Medwin
Letter to Edward Quillinan
12 October 1846
THE WORDSWORTH TRUST

Medwin makes it clear that he is publishing against the wishes of the Shelley family. What he emphasizes to his friend Quillinan (Wordsworth's son-in-law) was that Shelley wished Southey might approve of him even though there were clearly ideological and temperamental differences.

...My life of Shelley is now in the Press - I have received the first three Sheets for correction - I regret with you that Mrs Shelley should have indiscriminately printed & reprinted much of her Husband's Prose - Especially his early crudities - & that she left unexpurged several passages in his Letters. - When some of the Essays of his were written he had not begun to be a Platonist.

Generally speaking near relations make bad Biographers from their partiality - the blindness of their affection - I had intended my Life of Shelley for Moxon but heard that the *Life* would be submitted in the first instance to Mrs Shelley - an insuperable barrier to my publishing with him. - She wrote to me to deprecate the publication in any shape, and perhaps I should have felt inclined to comply with her wishes but that I had already made an Engagement with Newby.

- I was at Pisa when Shelley wrote to Southey as an Influential person in the conduct of the Quarterly - appealing to him against the review of Endymion. (by the way Monkton Milnes is occupied in writing Keats' Life). I saw Southey's reply which alluded to something that past at Keswick when Shelley was there with his first wife whose fate was so appalling - The Letter affected Shelley deeply & I have to attend to this but have treated Shelley's relations with Southey as lightly & with as much delicacy as I could - The only time I ever saw Southey was at Chantry's when he was sitting to the Sculptor for his Bust, an admirable one - Southey's Life will make an interesting piece of biography - a totally different one from Shelley's which reads like one entire Romance.

196
Edward Dowden
The Life of Percy Bysshe Shelley
London: Kegan, Paul, Trench & Co., 1886
PRIVATE COLLECTION

Dowden's *Life of Shelley* prompted Arnold to exclaim dismissively in print: 'What a set!' It was the Victorian climate of moral rigour that made Shelley all the more seem 'an ineffectual angel beating in the void his luminous wings in vain'. A more tolerant age, as the late twentieth century may think itself, has found ways of appreciating Shelley's honesty in his private life.

197
Leigh Hunt
Letter to Lord Byron
July 1823
JOHN MURRAY COLLECTION

Leigh Hunt's quarrels with Byron after the death of Shelley can be explained in part by the uneasiness of the aristocrat with the middle-class Leigh Hunt. Hunt's insistence here on justice for himself and his family, and his sense that Shelley would have protected him, shows moral courage. Byron himself was moved to be more accommodating to Hunt's wishes to stay in Italy and his hopes of living more economically.

. . . I confess it does astonish me, that even with reference to those notions and much more on a thousand higher accounts, you could suffer yourself to speak in such a manner of Shelley & his conscious, especially after what you yourself have said of the supereminence of his nature, and of the natures, origin, & what not, of the persons, whom you are now pleased to contrast with us all in a manner so new and admonitory. I have altered a word here, that my tone might not be mistaken. I cannot but hope & believe, that upon reflection you will have wished me to [?] in the feelings which your mention of my friends has excited, & which accordingly very soon subsided in me to give way to relection on my own past; but there is one passage in your letter, which will, at all events, excuse me for saying, that should my friend, after all his hard struggles in the cause of humanity, be destined to have a new & most inspected hand, however formidable, laid upon his drowned head, the occasion will gift me with all the anger, & perhaps with all the powers, necessary to make the blow repeated, - and this, not as you seem to put it, because he was merely my friend & therefore to be defended at all hazards, but because he was the friend of all the world, and died daily, inch by inch, in their cause. To anticipate, a second time, a proper & homourable interpretation of this announcement in your Lordship's mind, would, I trust, be paying an ill compliment to the actual feelings on both sides.

Cat. 198

198
Robert Browning (1812-89)
Portrait by Carlo Pellegrini ('Ape')
Published 29 November 1875
Print 30.9 x 18.4 cms
THE WORDSWORTH TRUST

In 1826 the fourteen year-old Robert Browning purchased Benbow's pirated *Miscellaneous Poems* of Shelley (1826), and was so affected by it that for two years became an atheist and a vegetarian. His youthful enthusiasm for the poet is expressed in his early poem, *Pauline*.

199
Percy Bysshe Shelley
Letters of Percy Bysshe Shelley (with an introductory essay by Robert Browning)
London: Edward Moxon, 1852
THE BRITISH LIBRARY BOARD

In 1852 Edward Moxon published twenty-five letters supposedly written by Shelley, and Robert Browning agreed to write a preface. Unknown to Browning (and to Moxon), these letters were forgeries by De Gibler, an obsessed literary nuisance who called himself 'Major Byron'. 'I have just got a letter from a person who signs himself *George Gordon Byron* & says I must now be aware that he is the son of the *Poet*', wrote Thomas Medwin to Edward Quillinan in 1846, 'This is entirely new to me. - What Planet can he have dropt from? Did you ever hear of Byron's having a son? He says he is writing a work on Byron & has some papers of Schilling's . . . Who could his mother have been'.

The letters were revealed as forgeries when F.T. Palgrave recognised part of a *Quarterly* article by his own father in a letter supposed to have been written by Shelley to Godwin twenty-one years before. Thomas Love Peacock later confirmed that they were not genuine. This copy is evidence of Moxon's gratitude and embarassment; it is inscribed: 'Fras. Palgrave his book. Given me by Mr Moxon when he suppressed the publication.'

200
Robert Browning
Letter to Edward Dowden
Venice, 12 October 1883
THE BRITISH LIBRARY BOARD

Browning here reports on his having seen certain letters from Harriet which showed her sense of trauma in being left by Shelley. Again and again, biographical details, often from only one point of view, emerge to shock Shelley's admirers.

It is only when a kaleidoscope of all the participants is assembled that one can see that history is more than a matter of heroes and villains. What all biographies of Shelley can do is emphasise that his poetry is based upon everyday experience. Platonist and idealist Shelley may have been, but the strength of his poetry is that he is also aware that his feet have not left the ground.

My dear Mr Dowden,
   I got a letter of yours addressed to Mr. Furnivall, containing a request that I would give you some further information of the matters I mentioned to him. As to what Mr. Hookham told me in the only conversation we had, I prefer keeping silence about stories for the truth of which he only was responsible, and which I heard some twenty-five years ago. But the letters which he showed me were good evidence on certain points misunderstood, or mis-stated, in every account I had previously seen. Harriet represented as either uneducated or incapable of becoming so said

that, in compliance with her husband's desire, she was learning Latin, and could already make out the Odes of Horace. She was, for the same reason, practising music, and commissioned Hookham to procure for her pieces `especially by Mozart'. The most striking letter was the last one written to enquire where Shelley might be, whether as the writer thought probable, with Hookham altogether conceived in such a state of surprise and bewilderment at his disappearance as to completely dispose of the notion, hitherto accepted by Shelley's biographers, that they had parted by common consent, the wife proving in the sequel unable to bear the separation as philosophically as her husband. I was not responsible for Rossetti's statement about the destitution in which she was left.

Hookham said Shelley was suffering from intense bodily pain at the time `would roll himself suddenly on the ground, pulling the sofa-cushions upon him' and, to alleviate this, `he would actually go about with a laudanum bottle in his hand, supping thence as need might be'. The letter containing the account of the imaginary nocturnal attack was begun, for perhaps three lines, by Shelley, and the rest added, from his version of it, by the wife. All the letters were well written in every respect.

This is all I am able to say, and, of course, is for you and not the public my object in saying it being to refer you to documents which must still be in existence, and ought to be produced if the controverted subject of Shelley's relations with his first wife is to be raised. I write in great hast, but with all the good wishes which go to you in leisure from
Yours truly ever,
Robert Browning.

201*
Percy Bysshe Shelley
Bust attributed to Marianne Hunt
Wood H 43 cms
ETON COLLEGE

Marianne Hunt, the wife of Leigh Hunt, was an amateur sculptor and maker of silhouettes. At one time owned by Robert Browning, this bust is now at Eton College.

Trelawny thought it a bad general likeness, but Leigh Hunt pronounced its accuracy to be 'at times . . . startling', and certainly, with its downcast eyes and middle-aged features, it presents a more believable image of Shelley than the 'angelic' portraits of Curran and Clint. The mercurial quality of Shelley's appearance is described by Medwin:

I should conceive of no one so difficult to pourtray, the expression of his countenance being ever flitting and varied, - now depressed and melancholy, now lit up like that of a spirit, - making him look one moment forty and the next eighteen.

The artist's husband, Leigh Hunt, published a description of Shelley in 1838 in the *Literary and Pictorial Repository*, which is in accord with the bust:

This great poet . . . was about five feet ten or eleven in height, and peculiarly slim, so as to give him an aspect even of fragility. His hair and complexion were light, the face finer than the handsomest could possibly be. The eyes were produced, watchful, and full of the most

Cat. 203

impassioned feeling; brilliant, yet of a mild thoughtfulness which softened what would otherwise have been their wild expression. The nose was straight and small, and finely carved; the mouth narrow, the lip protruding, the upper one being, a sculptor might think, too long; but it was at all events not sufficiently so to mar the sensitiveness and tremulous firmness (if I may be allowed the expression) which characterized it. The chin receded, and was small and pointed. The cheeks were slightly sunken; the forehead was broad, but not intellectual in the phrenological sense of the word.'

202
Percy Bysshe Shelley
Portrait after A. Curran (engr. M. & N. Hanhart)
23 January 1867
Lithograph H 48 cms
DAVID ALEXANDER COLLECTION

During the latter part of the nineteenth century a number of engravings of Shelley appeared based on the portrait by Amelia Curran, each enhancing the angelic impression of the original. Some who knew the poet found in these images a distortion of the truth, but for others they were not angelic enough. 'The engraved portraits of Bysshe, which have hitherto been published,' wrote Shelley's sister Hellen to her sister Jane, 'are frightful pictures for a spiritual being, like the poet.'

203
Thomas Moore (1779-1852)
Portrait by Sir Thomas Lawrence
No date
Oil on canvas 73 x 61 cms
JOHN MURRAY COLLECTION

Cat. 202

Thomas Moore was a poet famous for his *Irish Melodies* (published 1807-34), and Byron's first biographer. He never met Shelley, but clearly admired him. In a letter to Mary Shelley of 3 September 1829 he wrote:

> I find Shelly [*sic*] not so easily dealt with as I expected - such men are not to be dispatched in a sentence. But you must leave me to manage it in my own way - I must do with him, as with Byron - blink nothing (that is, nothing but what is ineffable) - bring what I think *shadows* fairly forward, but in such close juxtaposition with the *lights*, that the latter will carry the day. This is the way to do such men real service.

204
The Shelley Monument
By Edward Onslow Ford
1894
Photograph 27.5 x 19 cms
UNIVERSITY COLLEGE, OXFORD

A statue commissioned by University College, more than half a century after Shelley's death.

205
Stopford Brooke
Inaugural Address to the Shelley Society
Private printing: 1886
DEREK WISE COLLECTION

Stopford Brooke replies to Arnold's description of Shelley as 'an ineffectual angel':

> Were society to alter, as it must soon alter or disintegrate, away from this condition, and live more in the hopes, and with the aims, and in the simple life, of Shelley, and along with these possess also his sanity of view, it would then understand how foolish it is to call him "a beautiful, but ineffectual angel, beating in the void his luminous wings in vain." Towards that change, his work in poetry concerning man is one element of power; but I fear that those who move too far apart from the more ideal hopes of man, in the midst of a formulated culture, will not see or understand that this is true. . . . If you wish to be in the forefront of the future, if you wish to live in the ideas which will, thirty years hence, rule the world, live among the men who are indignant and who hope with Shelley, who have his faith, who hear the trumpet of a prophecy, and whose cry day and night is this -
>
> > O wind,
> > If winter comes, can spring be far behind

Select Bibliography

Texts of Shelley's Works

Clark, David Lee, *Shelley's Prose*, London, 1988

Hutchinson, Thomas (Ed.), *Shelley Poetical Works*, new edn, corrected by G.M. Matthews, London, 1970

Jones, Frederick L. (Ed.), *Mary Shelley's Journal*, Oklahoma, 1947

Jones, Frederick L. (Ed.), *The Letters of Percy Bysshe Shelley*, Oxford, 1964

Reiman, Donald H. and Powers, Sharon B. (Eds.), *Shelley's Poetry and Prose*, New York, 1977

Other Works

Barcus, James E. (Ed.), *Shelley, The Critical Heritage*, London, 1975

Bishop, Franklin, *Polidori! A Life of Dr John Polidori*, The Gothic Society, 1991

Bloom, Harold, *Shelley's Mythmaking*, New York, 1969

Burnett, T.A.J., *The Rise and Fall of a Regency Dandy*, Oxford, 1983

Butler, Marilyn, *Romantics, Rebels and Reactionaries*, Oxford, 1981

Cameron, Kenneth Neil and Reiman, Donald H. (Eds.), *Shelley and His Circle* (Vols. I-VI), London and Cambridge, Mass., 1961-1973

Cameron, Kenneth Neill, *The Young Shelley, Genesis of a Radical*, London, 1951

Cameron, Kenneth Neill, *Shelley: The Golden Years*, Cambridge, Mass., 1974

Chesser, Eustace, *Shelley & Zastrozzi: self-revelation of a neurotic*, London, 1965

Curry, Kenneth (Ed.), *New Letters of Robert Southey* (2 Vols.), New York and London, 1965

Foot, Paul, *Red Shelley*, London, 1980

Forman, Maurice Buxton, *The Letters of John Keats*, Oxford, 1931

Gittings, Robert, *John Keats*, London, 1968

Gittings, Robert and Manton, Jo, *Claire Clairmont and the Shelleys 1798-1879*, Oxford, 1992

Grylls Glynn, R., *Claire Clairmont*, London, 1939

Griggs, Earl Leslie (Ed.), *Collected Letters of Samuel Taylor Coleridge*, Oxford, 1959

Hogg, Thomas Jefferson, *The Life of Percy Bysshe Shelley* (2 Vols.), London, 1858

Holmes, Richard, *Shelley, The Pursuit*, London, 1974

Jones, Frederick L. (Ed.), *The Letters of Mary W. Shelley*, Oklahoma, 1944

Marchand, Leslie A., *Byron's Letters and Journals*, London, 1973-1982

O'Neill, Michael, *Percy Bysshe Shelley. A Literary Life*, London, 1989

Redpath, Theodore, *The Young Romantics and Critical Opinion 1807-1824*, London, 1973

Rossetti, William Michael, *The Diary of Dr. John William Polidori*, London, 1911

Sperry, Stuart, *Shelley's Major Verse. The Narrative and Didactic Poetry*, Cambridge, Mass., 1988

Stocking, Marion Kingston (Ed.), *The Journals of Claire Clairmont*, Cambridge, Mass., 1968

Tomalin, Claire, *Mary Wollstonecraft*, London, 1974

Tomalin, Claire, *Shelley and His World*, London, 1980

Trelawny, Edward John, *Records of Shelley, Byron and the Author*, London, 1973

Webb, Timothy, *Shelley: A voice not understood*, New Jersey, 1977

White, Newman Ivey, *Shelley*, London, 1947

Wise, T.J., *Catalogue of the Ashley Library*, London, 1924

Yeats, W.B., *Essays and Introductions*, London, 1961